A HOUSE THAT Grace BUILT

Workbook & Journal

by Stephanie Tucker

A House that Grace Built Workbook and Journal
by Stephanie Tucker

Published by:
Spirit of Life Recovery Resources
18652 Florida Street, Suite 200
Huntington Beach, CA 92648

Publisher Notes:
Disclaimer:
A House that Grace Built Workbook and Journal is not necessarily intended to diagnose or treat your individual issues. If you are in a serious or life threatening situation, please get professional help immediately. This book is in no means intended to replace the need for professional and/or medical treatment. You are reading this book as an opinion, with scriptural references to verify the biblical reference of the principles that are contained.

This book is a culmination of personal experience, the Word of God, books, teaching and other resources written or watched over the years. Every effort was made to assure this book was written with original material and is not infringing or copying someone else's work. If you find editorial errors, please contact the publisher.

Printed in the United States of America

*Dedicated to the men and women partaking of this process
who are ready and willing to rebuild. May God have His way!*

INTRODUCTION

☙

Learning how to bring things from our head to the heart is no easy task. That's because we can't actually understand spiritual principles in our mind alone. We are need of God's Spirit in us to interpret them on our behalf. Therefore, our connection to God is more important than actually completing the projects this workbook contains! With that being understood, I developed this workbook to aid and assist in the "processing" of the material taught in *A House that Grace Built*. This book should not be read stand-alone, as it will offer little insight into the depth of each subject. Rather, I encourage that each chapter in *A House that Grace Built* be read first. Furthermore, I strongly recommend that you read and complete *The Christian Codependence Recovery Workbook: From Surviving to Significance* prior to attempting to proceed with this process. It offers the first stage of recovery that is necessary to continue with the "building" process.

While I have seen tremendous growth as a result of these application projects, each person going through this workbook will have unique needs. Therefore, I encourage you to evaluate your needs, your timing and the personal necessity of each task. Remember, it's not in the external "doing" where we are set free. If you feel bound and constrained by this homework process instead of empowered by it, it will greatly lose its impact. That's because it's only meant to facilitate a dialogue that you are having with the Lord. It's also meant to help expose your issues, and equip you with tools that can aid in learning how to deal with various relationship challenges.

Of everything that is taught, I fully believe that the very most important aspect in this workbook process is your time spent alone with God. That's because above anything else, you need to discover His personal interest in you, the plans He has for you and the power of His actual presence in your life. You need God to be real and His truth to be tangibly visible in your life. Above all, you need to make choices for yourself, learning to understand how to respond from God's Spirit, not just human influence or process.

I pray that you would enjoy and be blessed in the journey. Find plenty of freedom and grace in it, with a willingness to let God have all of you. Believe that He can bring you into a new life based on the power of His grace alone. The result will be something beautiful, secure and built for eternity.

Now all glory to God, who is able, through his mighty power at work within us, to accomplish infinitely more than we might ask or think. - Ephesians 3:20

In His grace,

Stephanie Tucker

TABLE OF CONTENTS
The chapter name for the each application project is identical to A House that Grace Built.

CHAPTER 1
THE TASK OF REBUILDING

Based on Chapter 1 of *A House that Grace Built*

Rebuilding denotes that something had once been in place, but needs to be constructed again. The reason something requires rebuilding can vary. Sometimes an upgrade is desired; destruction of the former structure is necessary in order to create a more elegant or modern replacement. But other times, devastating and heartbreaking damage has caused deep levels of loss and pain. The trauma of an unexpected "storm" of life can seemingly shake and rock everything we once held dear. How we approach the two realities that something is being torn down in our lives, and something is being rebuilt, will offer us insight into how we need to continue to heal and grow.

If what we are leaving behind is deeply painful and a sense of loss is overwhelming, God must assure us and anchor us in the hope of what He desires to do in and through us. God doesn't merely take away, He purifies and gives life to that which is broken. He isn't necessarily asking us to give up things or people, but to let go of an entire mentality. He wants us to *stop surviving*, and to *start living* and dreaming of a life orchestrated and designed by Him.

Chapter Highlights

- Assessing recovery
- Rebuilding with love
- Understanding the Holy Spirit
- Developing a throne room

Homework Purpose

In this next phase of recovery, we want to understand where we have been and where we are going. We need to assess the level of security we gained in knowing the love of God, and see how the lifestyle of God dependency has affected us thus far. If we struggle in this area, we want to learn about the areas of vulnerability, so God can continue to heal and purify our heart, soul and spirit.

Assessing Our Recovery

When we embrace recovery, we are able to walk through life with God's resources rather than attempt to survive through our own strategies. As God begins to mature and grow us, we discover that there is much more work to be done, and many more places to heal. That's why this "building project" will take the rest of our lives here on earth! God doesn't require that we are perfect, but that we are dependent and willing to be obedient. He understands our weaknesses, and therefore offers grace to deal with each need that is revealed.

Describe where you were spiritually before entering recovery. How did you deal with your needs?

_____

_____

_____

Can you describe a time when you looked at "rubble" and realized the life you were living was broken? What was it like to face that?

_____

_____

_____

How do you feel when you think of living the lifestyle of grace and being prepared for a future God's way? Are you scared? Are you excited?

_____

_____

_____

What continues to bring you back into the former lifestyle of survival? Are you are having a difficult time releasing anything in your recovery?

_____

_____

_____

Rebuilding Through Love

Understanding God's love in our minds is always different than receiving it in our hearts. We learned in Chapter 1 that we don't just need to know that God loves us; we must receive that love and have it work its way into us in a real and tangible way. Based on some of the principles we learned in Chapter 1, let's reflect on some of the key components of love.

Do I see how God is bringing me into truth? What specifically has been revealed to me recently that I could not see before?

_____

_____

_____

Do I feel God is involved in my life right now, and that I can feel secure because He is in control? Is He "shaking" up former securities so that I can no longer depend on "things" and people?

_____

_____

_____

Do I see and feel my identity in Him? Are there barriers that block this, or remnants of my old survival lifestyle that prevent this?

_____

_____

_____

Do I feel a deeper sense of conviction? Am I seeing a deeper layer of my internal brokenness, understanding Jesus has the total remedy for it?

_____

_____

_____

Do I live in the reality of grace, or do I still measure myself by performance?

_____

_____

_____

Do I see people differently? Can I have compassion for people, while hating their behaviors?

_____

_____

_____

Have I encountered intimacy with God?

_____

_____

_____

UNDERSTANDING THE HOLY SPIRIT

Many times we greatly misunderstand that the Holy Spirit is a Person and that He works in a variety of ways to heal, transform, and conform us to the image of God. Assessing your own understanding and belief in the Holy Spirit is critical. It will help you know if you are unintentionally grieving Him.

What is your understanding of the Holy Spirit?

_____

_____

_____

Have you ever felt afraid or confused about His position in your life? Have you ever rejected the notion of relying on the Holy Spirit—pretending you experienced Him—when in truth, you did not?

_____

_____

_____

Action Steps
1. Do your own Bible study on the Holy Spirit. Ask God to deal with any confusion or difficulties you have understanding Him.
2. Embrace and choose to find one principle each day about the Holy Spirit that you want to use in your life experience right now.

DEVELOPING A THRONE ROOM

In this journey we must learn how to access God and feed off His power and His resources. Talking about that is one thing, actually experiencing it is another. Learning to develop a faith-based intimate walk with the Lord isn't something we do through any particular format—we must do it in our hearts. But developing quality alone time with God where we are committed to engaging in communication with Him will help us build a solid foundation.

Action Steps

1. Write a list of your expectations about what you believe God can and will do in your life. These are things you are willing to hang onto even when circumstances don't necessarily match. Pray over the list and ask God to change it as needed. Believe God can, is able, and desires to bring you into completion.

2. Ask God to help you go to Him first before involving yourself in day-to-day interactions. This discipline will help you learn to put God over and above human relationships. You may want to leave a note in a prominent place that says: "Remember, God's love first will give me what I need to love in my relationships."

3. Prepare a throne room in your heart that is reserved for all the issues and challenges that will be dealt with through this workbook and in your life experiences. However you visualize it, the throne room will be the place where you lay things down that concern, hurt, or cause you pain. It will also be a place where you offer praise, thanksgiving, and worship. But mostly, it will be a place of rest and waiting. A place you can go to find stability during the "messiness" of construction.

4. Follow a daily reading plan in God's Word. This is not to be done in a religious way—but it's to allow God to minster to you. This will give you the chance to personally hear from Him. A suggested reading plan is listed in the journal, but you are free to do any plan of your choosing.

5. Begin a daily journey and log the interactions taking place in your "throne room (See journal beginning on page 139). In your journal, log those things that you are receiving from God, either through your reading in the Word or practical everyday experiences. In the other area of your journal, track what you need to give to God, including whatever burdens or challenges you. These are things you must "lay down" and surrender. You will be praying and asking God for help with these issues. Also include any words of thanks, praise, worship and affection towards Him. One of the ways we love God is through our willingness to be obedient to Him. Track anything substantial in this area of your life.

6. On a weekly basis, write one truth or promise that is revealed to you. Speak and claim that promise as your own, expecting God to respond to it.

An example of a throne room journal is provided on page 139 that you can use while you are completing this workbook. You can also create your own.

CHAPTER 2
A SEASON OF PREPARATION

Based on Chapter 2 of *A House that Grace Built*

When we are preparing for something, we are getting ready for its arrival. For example, we prepare food so that we can eat a dinner. Or, we prepare for a career through a formal education that will give us the skills needed to succeed. Therefore, whenever we use the word "preparation," it by default means that we are expecting something to be accessed once the necessary tasks are completed.

Recovery is no different. We are preparing to walk with new tools, a changed perspective, and a God-given destination. The specifics of how that may look in our own lives varies. But we can be certain of one thing—God is preparing us for lifestyles of God dependency where we are trusting Him, seeking Him, and learning how to become aligned with the calling and purpose He has ordained.

The season of preparation can be the most difficult as we step out of bondage and into obedience to God. That's because everything in our lives will be unknown, and usually God doesn't make the specifics of His plans clear immediately. But in this season of preparation, He is doing something in our hearts and lives that is inconceivable. God is preparing us, shaping us, molding us, and forming His character into us.

Chapter Highlights
- Releasing and receiving
- Grief that heals
- Seasons of waiting

Homework Purpose

Chapter 2 exposed some of the training and equipping that takes place while we are waiting. Above anything, we need to get in touch with those issues that require release and surrender, as well as learn how to feel a healthy and healing form of grief. The projects are intended to help us process through the various "in between" places we may find ourselves in throughout our recovery, providing us with stabilizing hope and security in the faithfulness of God.

WHAT WE HOLD ONTO

Learning how to give our issues to the Lord rather than attempt to control, fix or manage them on our own is one the most important transitions we will make in recovery. Being able to implement this into our lives may take time. Based on the lesson in Chapter 2, respond to each issue listed below and see if you can recognize when or if you have released the issues to God. If not, write the reason why you continue to hold on. If you have released, explain how you are feeling about it right now. Finally, pray over it and write it in your "throne room" as something you are ready and willing to surrender at the feet of Jesus.

Relationships. These can be current or past relationships that we continually focus on and try to fix or change. We think, dwell, reflect, and focus on them so much, they have ownership in our lives to an extent. These aren't healthy connections, but relationships that are filled with challenges that we ourselves desire to overcome, or have gotten to the point where we realize the need for God's help.

_____

_____

_____

Things. Material possessions sometimes help build a sense of security. We may place a high value on buying new things, or even "storing" excess amounts of food or other necessities out of fear of running out. We may find ourselves attached to certain possessions we own, and the thought of losing them may be devastating.

_____

_____

_____

Our Outward Reputation/Image. We can continue to hold onto the outside persona we have tried to project to other people. We may have tremendous fear at the thought of something being revealed in our lives that would project our outward identities in a "weak" or negative light.

_____

_____

_____

Positions. We may cling to a position of responsibility, authority, or leadership as validation of our personal worth. This can include our involvement in ministry or our vocational career. Having these responsibilities is perfectly legitimate, but when the thought of losing them brings a sense of total loss of self, it's an indication that we clutch onto it in an unhealthy way for security.

_____

_____

_____

Financial Security. We can either be overcome with fear of not being able to provide for ourselves financially, or driven to earn more and more. When our abilities to earn money drives our entire lives, without a deeper sense of God as our Provider, this can indicate a false security system in place that needs to be released.

_____

_____

_____

Guilt and Shame. If we haven't properly dealt with guilt and shame, they will continue to latch onto our souls in an unhealthy way, causing us to see ourselves wrongly, feel "inward contamination," and thus try to "undo" its effects. Guilt and shame are always dealt with through the blood of Jesus Christ and never have a legitimate place in our lives.

_____

_____

_____

Addiction. In addition to our codependence, we may have other addictions that we are attempting to overcome. They may include food, sex, alcohol, drugs, gambling, cigarettes, etc. Anything that is dominating and "owning" us in an unhealthy way will interfere with any future growth. Sometimes we need a deeper level of intervention or help to assist us in this process. Be sure to ask for help.

_____

_____

_____

WHAT ARE YOU GRIEVING?

Grieving is the process where we purge the deep hurt and pain over the losses in our lives. Through healthy grief we can experience healing and properly move beyond difficult circumstances and challenges. Learning to grieve is also about forming a new coping mechanism where we learn to feel our feelings and openly and honestly deal with our pain before the Lord. No one can tell us how or what we must grieve, we must allow God to direct our hearts and minds. Take some time to note the following (use the worksheet on page 18):

1. Things I need to grieve but haven't yet
2. Things I am currently grieving
3. Things I have grieved already

THINGS I'M GRIEVING WORKSHEET

THINGS I NEED TO GRIEVE BUT HAVEN'T	THINGS I AM CURRENTLY GRIEVING	THINGS I HAVE GRIEVED ALREADY
_____	_____	_____

Action Step

Bring this list into your "throne room" with God, pray over these issues, and ask Him to connect you to whatever you need in order to move ahead.

Developing a New Coping Mechanism

Grief is not something to be dreaded, but a tool God gives us to cope with loss in a healthy way. When we grieve with God, we have access to His comfort and the power of His Spirit. In all of our heartbreaking and difficult scenarios, God wants to teach us how to cope effectively through Him. By coping, we will be able to avoid the pitfalls of codependence, substance addiction, or other compulsive behaviors that manifest by seeking false comfort.

Action Steps
1. As you face difficult and painful situations, place them in your journal. Practice the discipline of going before God with these issues in your day-to-day interactions. When you "act out" in your codependence, use it as an opportunity to transition that situation into a "grief and release."
2. Meditate on God's truth in the midst of your pain.

Waiting for God

Waiting is one of the most difficult disciplines we are asked to engage in, yet most of our lives we will be spent in some form of a "waiting room." To help you better cope, it's important to get in touch with what you are longing for, waiting upon, and anticipating to occur. Understanding this also helps you to remember to continually bring these issues before the King, instead of reverting to wrongful ways to manipulate the outcome.

Action Steps
1. Write a list of the things you are currently waiting for or longing for.
2. Pray over each issue for God to purify, cleanse, and provide guidance and direction.

Waiting List:

_____

_____

_____

_____

_____

_____

_____

_____

_____

_____

_____

_____

_____

_____

_____

_____

_____

_____

_____

_____

_____

_____

_____

_____

_____

_____

_____

_____

_____

_____

_____

_____

_____

_____

_____

_____

_____

_____

_____

_____

CHAPTER 3
THE FRAMEWORK OF GROWTH

Based on Chapter 3 of *A House that Grace Built*

Growth takes time. That's because the massive process of recovery and reprogramming is working to renew our minds, our hearts, our thoughts, our attitudes, our beliefs, our emotions, and ultimately our choices and behaviors. What we bring with us into recovery will determine what it will take in order for us to become realigned with God's purposes. For some of us, we have never encountered our authentic identities. We had serious distortions in the "data" that was fed into our minds from a young age; thus, the sorting and cleaning of our minds and lives may require a more lengthy process.

Whenever we begin a journey, we want the hope that the destination is attainable—and we will indeed get to where we want to go. Our journey of recovery is going to require significant patience and a constant willingness to let God dig deeper and deeper into our souls and extract anything that holds us, binds us, or prevents us from His perfect will.

Chapter Highlights

- Understanding the growth process mentally, emotionally and spiritually
- Leaving home
- Assessing growth in recovery

Homework Purpose

This chapter helps us understand our recovery goals, how we attain those goals, and some of the deeper truths of how we actually do change. In this homework, you want to get in touch with your own growth processes and how you learned to cope and deal with life in the past. In place of faulty coping mechanisms, God wants to lead you into a transformational process— where the entire system of your life is impacted by obtaining the "mind of Christ." Remember, God doesn't just want your behavior to change; He wants your heart to change!

UNDERSTANDING OUR DEVELOPMENT

In this chapter, we looked at the deeper influences that affected us as we were raised and brought through life. Because these often became automatic learned beliefs and relationship styles, it is helpful to understand each area in more detail. By confronting each area, we are better equipped to note the areas of our lives that are vulnerable or are in need of a continual process of renewal.

UNDERSTANDING THE FUNCTION OF OUR MINDS

Our minds are where we accumulated information and developed belief systems. Assess the following questions:

What lies in the past most impacted you? What is actual truth?

_____

_____

_____

What principle about the mind have you learned that you can apply to your life right now?

_____

_____

_____

UNDERSTANDING THE FUNCTION OF EMOTIONS

Our emotional equipping occurred by the way we were taught to handle and deal with our feelings. Assess the following questions:

How were feelings expressed in your home? How did you learn to cope with them?

_____

_____

_____

Describe any memory you might have of your emotional issues as a child. Do you remember how a parent assisted you?

_____

_____

_____

How do you deal with your emotional issues right now? Do you feel the real feeling? How do you cope with it? Do you find yourself continuing to repress?

_____

_____

_____

Explain what you learned to help you better deal with your emotions. What principle can you apply right now?

_____

_____

_____

_____

_____

_____

_____

UNDERSTANDING THE FUNCTION OF THE WILL

Our will reflects the area in our lives where we make choices. Depending on how our will was developed, we may have experienced various forms of bondage. Assess the following:

How was your will managed as a child? Was it controlled? Were you disciplined? Did you have the ability to make choices?

_____

_____

_____

How did you view your will into adulthood? Did you feel you had the right to make choices? Did you seek other people's approval? Did you give over "decision making" to someone else?

_____

_____

_____

Have you assigned God the authority of your will? What does that look and feel like?

_____

_____

_____

Leaving Home

As we will discover in later chapters, a detachment process happens throughout childhood that prepares us to eventually live life apart from parental dependencies. Oftentimes in dysfunctional systems, we continue to recycle the painful elements of childhood (if applicable). We may not know how to see ourselves or live life apart from the identity and circumstances we faced in our families of origin.

This next project is extremely valuable in helping us gently detach from the past. It isn't meant to disrespect the role our parents had in our lives, but to acknowledge our maturity, and say good-bye to our childhood. This enables us to prepare our hearts to be in adult relationships with our parents, siblings, etc. (if possible).

Action Steps

1. Write a letter to your little child that lived under your parental influence. Give that child permission to leave home and enter into adulthood as God intended. Thank that child for doing his or her best.
2. Ask the child to forgive the people that harmed him or her. You may need to do this with the multiple levels of growth in your life depending on when or where trauma was introduced. This might have to occur when you were five, eight, twelve, etc. because each of those "stages" of the little child may need the opportunity to forgive and release the past. This will not fit every scenario, but if you had an extremely difficult upbringing it is recommended. Also you may need the help of a counselor if any disassociation has occurred.
3. Pray for your parents, and when applicable, pray that God can recreate the relationship in a healthy adult manner, or provide you the wisdom you need to deal with it in a respectful and loving way.
4. When you are finished writing the letter and prayers, visualize a home where you lived as a child. Picture yourself taking God's hand and walking out the front door, gently closing the door behind. Say "good-bye."

Assessing Growth

Understanding we are in the process of growth should come as a great relief! We do not need to be perfect, yet God loves us enough to allow us to mature. God is moving us through a growth process, sometimes quickly, and othertimes slowly. We may sometimes not recognize the work He is doing. By assessing our growth, we can become aware of the areas of lives where God is working.

Please refer to page 50 in *A House that Grace Built*. With each of those principles mentioned, find where you lie in the "growth" process. Remember, the areas of weakness are not to cause shame, but to show you where God needs to help you. It will also help you to see your need to be "watered" and "fed" by God's love, spiritual resources, and the "food" of His Word.

On the scale on the next page lie opposing principles. Your job is to choose where you fall on the scale. Over time, as you go back and review this, you may specifically see where God is changing, growing, and developing you, so don't be discouraged! We all need to start at a beginning point!

CODEPENDENCE   GOD DEPENDENCY
(Choose 1-10, with 1 being closest to codependence, and 10 being closest to God dependency)

Survival   Love
1   2   3   4   5   6   7   8   9   10

Competence by Effort   Competence through Grace
1   2   3   4   5   6   7   8   9   10

Controlled by Emotions   Controlled by God's Promises
1   2   3   4   5   6   7   8   9   10

Low Self-esteem   Precious Value through God
1   2   3   4   5   6   7   8   9   10

Poor Boundaries/Enmeshment   Healthy Boundaries
1   2   3   4   5   6   7   8   9   10

No Sense of Identity   Identity in Christ
1   2   3   4   5   6   7   8   9   10

Attached Primarily to Human Relationships   Attached to God
1   2   3   4   5   6   7   8   9   10

Controlled by People   Controlled by God
1   2   3   4   5   6   7   8   9   10

Produce Negative Fruits   Produce Fruits of the Spirit
1   2   3   4   5   6   7   8   9   10

Living Unforgiven   Living Forgiven
1   2   3   4   5   6   7   8   9   10

APPLICATION POINTS
What did you learn specifically about your weaknesses?

_____

_____

_____

What did you learn specifically of where God has truly worked to change your heart in this season of your life?

_____

CHAPTER 4
THE POWER OF CONNECTION

Based on Chapter 4 of *A House that Grace Built*

We learned in Chapter 4 that a soul tie is a connection we make with another person physically, emotionally, spiritually or sexually. These soul ties can be healthy or unhealthy. They can also be deeply powerful in our lives, affecting our emotions, desires and choices. But most important, our soul ties are rooted in a spiritual influence. A healthy soul tie has God's love and resources motivating it; while an unhealthy soul tie can have demonic or fleshly influence.

Much of this workbook will be dealing with our relationships in very specific ways. But before we get in the details of relational roles, we want to take a look at the overall nature of soul ties, and the unhealthy attachments we may have acquired in our lifetimes. If we discover an unhealthy soul tie, we must remember that God isn't necessarily going to end the relationship. Rather, He wants to cease the flow of the unhealthy transmission of negative relationship issues.

As God prepares our hearts and lives to be fruitful, He desires to detach us from unhealthy soul ties, while allows us opportunities to grow in a healthy attachment to Him and others.

∽
Chapter Highlights
- Understanding soul ties
- Assessing unhealthy soul ties
- Breaking the power of soul ties

∽
Homework Purpose
In codependence we normally minimized the level of influence people had on our lives. We furthermore didn't understand the spiritual conflicts that were contained in some of our unhealthy relationships. By being willing to assess and look at each soul tie we have made, we can accurately see the relational difficulties we may have experienced. This gives us the opportunity to end unhealthy soul ties, while allowing our heart to be entirely free to make healthy connections with God and others.

BREAKING SOUL TIES

Pray and ask God to reveal all the people and important relationships throughout your life that have produced negative fruit or inflicted pain. Remember, breaking an unhealthy soul tie doesn't mean the person is going to leave our lives; it just means that we are going to break any way we've negatively connected to someone. If you've ever been violated, please be sure to include that person. Some of the common relationships are listed below. You can follow this list or write your own (use a separate piece of paper if necessary).

Childhood family members:
Mom
Dad
Grandparents
Siblings
Any other important figure

_____

_____

_____

_____

_____

_____

_____

Childhood years:
Teachers
Mentors
Friends
Violators

_____

_____

_____

_____

_____

_____

_____

_____

Adulthood years:
Spouse
Children
Boyfriend
Girlfriend
Important friendship
Violators
Romantic relationship
Sexual relationship

_____

_____

_____

_____

_____

Action Steps

1. Organize that list by breaking them down into different categories. Please note: some relationships will fall into several or all of the categories (see "Soul Ties Categories Worksheet" on page 30).

   o ***Mental soul ties***: define anyone with whom you shared an unhealthy mental soul tie (anyone who spoke into your life as the voice of truth).

   o ***Emotional soul ties:*** define anyone where emotional dependence or enmeshment was present.

   o ***Sexual soul ties:*** define anyone with whom you shared a sexual relationship outside of marriage (include violations).

   o ***Spiritual soul ties:*** define anyone who had a spiritual authority position in your life (who wasn't totally influenced by the Holy Spirit) and used God, religion, or the Bible in a wrongful way.

2. On that list, you have just identified the soul ties you have connected with in your lifetime. Now, take the chart on page 31 and list all the names on the sheet. The more impacting, the bigger you can write their names—or use different colors to highlight them.
3. As you look at this chart, draw a small line that represents a connection attached to that person. This represents the soul tie itself.

RENOUNCING AND CLEANSING THE SOUL TIE

Now that your lists and chart are developed, you will begin to deal with each specific person on the list. You may need to do this over an extended period of time or whatever you feel you can handle. Do not rush the process, and take each person listed seriously and personally. Do NOT try merge everyone in the same process. This will not be effective. The steps in this process include:

1. Complete the "Soul Tie Information Worksheet" (see page 32) for each person listed.
2. Pray specifically over each person listed on the worksheet (see the prayers listed on page 33).

SOUL TIE CATEGORIES

MENTAL

_____
_____
_____
_____
_____
_____
_____

EMOTION

_____
_____
_____
_____
_____
_____
_____
_____

SEXUAL

_____
_____
_____
_____
_____
_____
_____

SPIRITUAL

_____
_____
_____
_____
_____
_____
_____

DRAWING SOUL TIES

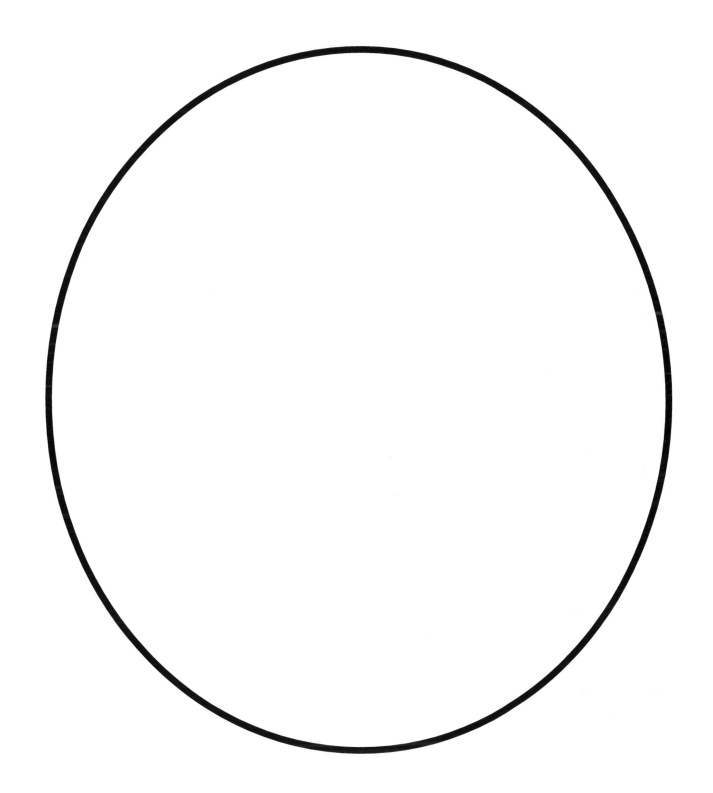

SOUL TIE WORKSHEET

Name of person: _____

Name the type of soul tie: _____

Name the overall nature of the relationship and the fruit it produced:

_____

_____

_____

Did you have wrongdoing for which you carry guilt?

_____

_____

_____

Were there violations for which you continue to feel anger, pain, or other hostile emotions?

_____

_____

_____

Were you born into the relationship (generational) or did you choose the relationship? (If inherited, be sure to refer to the prayer at the end of Chapter 3.)

_____

_____

_____

If you chose the relationship, why do you think you did so? What was the attraction?

_____

_____

_____

- Are you willing to renounce any unhealthy tie that was formed? _____
- Are you willing to allow God to purify the relationship through forgiveness and redemption, if He sees fit? _____
- Are you willing to release the relationship altogether if God sees fit? _____
- If yes, continue by praying over the soul tie through one of the prayers

SOUL TIE PRAYERS

A Prayer of Renunciation over Mental Soul Ties
Father God,

I come to You submitting my will to Yours. I place my thoughts and my mind under Your influence. I claim Your holy and perfect truth as the guiding influence of my life. I ask that You lead and guide me into all truths, and that You provide clarity and wisdom to know if or when I'm being deceived or mislead. Captivate and purify my entire mind, therefore, transforming me into Your image. I renounce any soul tie I created in giving _____ the right to speak truth into my life.

In my early family experience, I recognize that I had no choice, but into adulthood I did have choices. Therefore, I furthermore renounce any permission that I granted to spiritual influences through this soul tie. I announce that You are my Lord and Guide, and that You have full rights and access to my heart, my soul, and my life. Please place healthy people in my life who can affirm and uphold Your truth. Please protect my heart when forces attack my mind and try to take me from You. I love You and honor You as my King. If any demonic presence was given legal right as a result of this soul tie, I take back those rights and the permission that was granted. I command any spirit other than the Holy Spirit to be released in the name and authority of Jesus Christ.
In Jesus's name. Amen.

A Prayer of Renunciation of Emotional Soul Ties
Lord God, Heavenly Father,

I come to You clothed in the righteous standard of Your Son, Jesus Christ. I come under the power and authority of Him, declaring myself worthy and accepted in Your sight. Father, I have formed bonds and ties in my heart in human relationships that were not of You. I allowed my emotions to dictate my relationship more than my need for closeness with You. I have given myself over to friends and family, hoping that I could fill the inner pain and brokenness through them.

Lord God, I admit and repent of using people to satisfy my own needs. I fully acknowledge that the broken places in my soul only have one remedy—the life-giving resources of Your Spirit. Please cut and break me from any emotional dependency I have created with _____. Specifically, please help me to overcome _____. In my heart, I choose to place You in the position of being my decision-maker. Place people in my life who are healthy. Teach me how to love them, without needing them in unhealthy ways. Help me to learn to function interdependently as a member of Your body. If any demonic presence was given legal right as a result of this soul tie, I take back those rights and the permission that was granted. I command any spirit other than the Holy Spirit to be released in the name and authority of Jesus Christ.
In Jesus's name. Amen.
In Jesus's name. Amen.

A Prayer of Renunciation over Sexual Soul Ties – Through Choice
Lord God,

In the name of Jesus, I come clothed and prepared as the bride of Christ. I plead the blood of Jesus Christ over my heart and claim the inheritance I've been given in my relationship with Him. I admit that I have been unfaithful in the past and have allowed the precious right of my sexuality to be used improperly. In relating and trying to "love" another, I mistakenly gave up

what You hold in a very sacred regard for the earthly marriage relationship. I specifically did this with
_____. In the process, I dragged You through the merging of my body to him/her through sexual immorality. I know this hurt You, and it especially hurt me. Because I can't change what I've done, I ask that You forgive me and remove all the damage that was inflicted in my heart as a result. I pray that You would purify me into a renewed virginity. I pray that You give me a holy respect for this sacred area of my life, so that I can honor my own body and honor the marriage bed. I pray in the authority of Jesus Christ that any sexual demonic ties that had been formed through this relationship will be broken. If any demonic presence was given legal right as a result of this soul tie, I take back those rights and the permission that was granted. I command any spirit other than the Holy Spirit to be released in the name and authority of Jesus Christ.
In Jesus's name. Amen.

A Prayer of Renunciation over Sexual Ties – Through Violation
Father God,

The way _____ hurt me is inconceivable to me. I know that I didn't deserve or ask for this to occur—still in some ways, I have blamed myself. When he/she violated me, I felt that my preciousness and sacredness was lost. I felt ugly, dirty, and too disgusting for anyone to love. As a result, I can see that I brought this into my relationships with others where sex had a variety of distortions including _____. This violation prevented me from being able to connect and be intimate in a healthy way. I realize now that I was emotionally wounded and spiritually oppressed through this act. Because there is nothing that can be done to change it, I pray that You would remove the power that it placed on me. On the basis of Your forgiveness towards me, I choose to forgive _____, but I rebuke and condemn the sin. While I hate it, I place it under Your power to remove any further influence. I praise You for the marvelous and amazing gift of Your holy power and life working in me. I thank You that You are preparing me for a life of purity and wholeness. If any demonic presence was given legal right as a result of this soul tie, I take back those rights and the permission that was granted. I command any spirit other than the Holy Spirit to be released in the name and authority of Jesus Christ.

In Jesus's name. Amen.

A Prayer to Break Spiritual Ties and Connections
Lord God,

I place You in the position of authority in my life. I claim the authority that You have given me through the blood of Jesus Christ. I plead that blood and claim its power can far surpass any other spiritual connection I have made through a person. Please forgive me if I've looked to a human being as the source to satisfy my spiritual need. Please remove anyone who I've allowed wrongfully in a place of spiritual influence. Please help me to discern the nature of the spiritual authority I continually place in my life—and prepare me to walk on a pathway that will only lead me into the fullness and authenticity of the Holy Spirit.

I pray for my spiritual community that You've lead me into—may You be at the center of it and be glorified in it. If there are other demonic influences that have tried to steal Your glory and power, I pray in the name of Jesus that it would be brought down. I renounce any and every spiritual tie and connection that has been made outside of Your influence. I announce that as a child of Almighty God, I am empowered to live a life through Him based on His righteousness and truth.
In Jesus's name. Amen. If any demonic presence was given legal right as a result of this soul tie, I take back those rights and the permission that was granted. I command any spirit other than the Holy Spirit to be released in the name and authority of Jesus Christ. In Jesus's name. Amen.

CHAPTER 5
THE DESIGN OF INTIMACY

Based on Chapter 5 of *A House that Grace Built*

Throughout our lifetimes, we learned a variety of relationship skills that taught us how to be intimate and give and receive love. What we often didn't understand was the God-given purpose behind each human role, thus we didn't grasp God's designation for intimacy within our hearts.

In this chapter we began to see the purpose of intimacy, and placed a spiritual overlay of the temple of the Old Testament in order to better assess the positions of our own relationships. By learning how to see and picture our hearts in this manner, we can begin to understand where we may have made misappropriations of our affections.

Before our human relationships can be understood, we must start to get honest about our own intimacy issues with God. That's why we took an honest look at how God desires to engage in relationship with us, and how we can fail to give Him His rightful position in our lives.

Chapter Highlights
- Defining the role of intimacy
- Faulty intimacy styles with God
- Assessing idols

Homework Purpose
Understanding our intimacy styles with God and each other will significantly aid us to getting to the root of our issues. That's because this is where we are typically broken the most. Assessing where we are vulnerable to possessing an idol is key to accessing freedom.

This homework will allow us to expose any form of an idol in our heart, and help us to begin to understand the purpose and breakdown of intimacy.

UNDERSTANDING INTIMACY

Just as the rooms of a house contain different purposes, so our hearts also have rooms that hold unique purposes based on their God-ordained design. To help us gain God's perspective on intimacy, we looked at the "temple formula" of His house. This was modeled in the physical temple of the Old Testament where intimacy was divided in three distinct areas: Holy of Holies, inner court and outer court. By assessing our own "temple" in this same manner, we will be able see where our own intimacy issues have been misplaced or misappropriated.

FAULTY INTIMACY STYLES WITH GOD

In the Old Testament temple the dwelling place of God was called the Holy of Holies. As New Testament Christians, our Holy of Holies is a deep reservoir inside our heart set aside for intimacy with God. There are many ways this space can be misaligned with its purposes. Let's assess how our intimacy style with God may be misused or misunderstood.

What do you do to draw closer to the Lord? What do you think causes distance between you and Him?

_____

_____

_____

Can you identify any faulty belief systems you have regarding intimacy with Him?

_____

_____

_____

Have you used spiritual activity in place of time spent with Him, connecting and revealing the concerns of your heart?

_____

_____

_____

How do you interpret God's perspective towards you?

_____

_____

_____

ASSESSING IDOLS

Idols can be subtle and seemingly innocent. Yet as we draw close to God, we discover that anything we love or find security in more than God can constitute idolatry. Seeing this properly is not meant to condemn us, but to better address the distortions in our hearts. In truth, when we put others in the place reserved for God, we grieve the heart of God and misplace the purpose of human relationships. Let's take a look at how this may manifest in our own lives.

Where do I devote the majority of my inner life thoughts in a given day?

_____

_____

_____

Do I live for affection and attention of someone specifically—feeling either extremely excited when I receive it, or extremely distraught if I don't receive it?

_____

_____

_____

Is there a pattern of people pleasing in my life that drives me to win their hearts over to me?

_____

_____

_____

Who do I tie my own sense of happiness and wholeness to?

_____

_____

_____

Who or what makes up my sense of security?

_____

_____

_____

Who or what do I turn to for comfort?

_____

_____

_____

Once we are aware that we in fact have things that have taken God's place, the next step is that we actually learn how to remove those relationships and connections that have been made. Then we learn how to return God to His rightful position. In doing so, it does not by any means indicate that God will take those people out of our lives, but it does mean that we will need to re-prioritize our hearts. We will be systemically dealing with the unhealthy ties of human relationships in later chapters, but for now, here are some suggested projects.

Action Steps

1. Identify any idols that have been revealed and place them in your journal under the "What I Give to You" section.
2. Pray continually for God to purify your heart and for you to learn to go to Him first in all situations.

A Prayer for the Idols

Lord God,

I acknowledge that I've made _____ an idol in my heart. I did not mean for this to occur, but in all my sickness of codependence, I realize that I often placed people and things over you. I have not known You enough to even learn how to love and stay in intimate connection to You. Please help me with this. Please saturate my heart with a longing and deep affection to truly know You and love You.

Please show me how to operate from Your love and pour it into the people in my life. Please help me to release the idols and see them as people just like me who need You first. As Your beloved bride, I lay myself at Your feet and ask that you receive me, forgive me, and be positioned in first place in my heart. May You have all glory and honor in my life as I learn to enjoy living in the abundant privilege of marriage to You.

In Jesus's name. Amen.

CHAPTER 6
LEARNED INTIMACY SKILLS

Based on Chapter 6 of *A House that Grace Built*

O ur understanding of how to be close in human relationships was often first modeled through parenthood, but then emphasized and patterned in other relationships. Therefore, how we learned to connect and bond in relationships can oftentimes be traced back to our early life experiences. In this chapter, we sought to understand the intimacy patterns that emerged in our lives, particularly through our developmental years. These are typically the styles we eventually brought into our adulthood relationships.

While development is important, the older we grew, the more responsible we became for our own choices. Thus, while finding the roots is important, it does not by any means negate or lesson our own accountability in the situations. Just the same, if we are being asked to identify with painful or dysfunctional behavior, having a baseline understanding of what was acquired will assist us in being able to process, forgive and heal.

Chapter Highlights
- Intimacy with family of origin
- Intimacy with self
- Intimacy in friendship and dating

Homework Purpose

By identifying the source of skewed intimacy patterns, we can better understand those issues that have been deeply imbedded into our relationship styles today. God can eventually heal our intimacy styles by healing our hearts and teaching us to love His way. At this point in the process, we are simply attempting to recognize the problem, not necessarily apply the remedy. The homework application is designed to assist in this process.

INNER COURT RELATIONSHIPS

The inner courts of our hearts house the significant relationships throughout our lifetimes. Going into this area can be painful for some people, because it is oftentimes the place where we have been hurt the most. God wants to lead us into these areas in order to bring a complete healing, and to rid anything that was acquired through them in an unhealthy way. He doesn't ask that we rid those relationship, and always seeks an overall redemptive plan (See Chapter 10-14).

Overall, can you recognize intimacy dysfunction in how you connected in your inner court relationships during the developmental years?

_____

_____

_____

What significant relationships were lacking intimacy that you wanted to contain intimacy?

_____

_____

_____

Can you see how you used other outside relationships to try to replace that missing need?

_____

_____

_____

INTIMACY WITH PARENTS

Our parents interacted with us with their own set of intimacy patterns and styles; thus, they directly taught us relationship skills. While we do not need to blame our parents, we do want to understand the influence their intimacy patterns may have had upon our growth and development.

Can you identity where a breakdown occurred in intimacy development through your mother?

_____

_____

_____

Can you identify where a breakdown occurred in intimacy development through your father?

_____

_____

_____

Describe any negative intimacy skills that were introduced through your parents.

_____

_____

_____

Can you see these skills manifesting in your life right now? Explain specifically in which relationships and how.

_____

_____

_____

INTIMACY WITH OURSELVES

Many of us don't even know the point in our lives where we "lost ourselves." This loss of identity usually was formed at a young age, attached deeply to the root of codependence and caregiving. Understanding the disconnect we had with ourselves is an important part of recovery. God wants us to attach to our God-given person, and to know and love ourselves how He loves us.

How did you lose a sense of personal intimacy prior to recovery?

_____

_____

_____

Explain how well you know yourself at this point in your recovery?

_____

_____

_____

Can you pinpoint specific areas where you need to develop a deeper sense of personal intimacy?

_____

_____

_____

Do you recognize any compartmentalization? Are there areas of yourself you still hide in a form of protection? If so are you ready to ask God to break down the walls and allow you emerge as a whole person?

_____

_____

_____

SIBLING INTIMACY

Siblings are important relationships that set patterns of relationship styles at a young age. While our sibling relationships can dramatically change over time and seasons of life, it's helpful to see and comprehend their effect on us.

If applicable, explain how intimacy was portrayed or negated in your sibling relationships.

_____

_____

_____

How does that style of intimacy affect your relationship now?

_____

_____

_____

FRIENDSHIP AND DATING

As we began introducing relationships outside of our family system, we may have attached a variety of issues and needs onto them. Whether we sought to have missing needs validated, or unknowingly mimicked learned styles, our early friendships and dating styles are telling of what was happening in our hearts.

In what ways did you bond and attach in friendships? How did you draw close?

_____

_____

_____

In dating, describe the process you used to get to know someone. Was physical attraction a key factor? Was there spiritual intimacy or emotional honesty first?

_____

_____

_____

THE SACRED ROOMS OF FAMILY INTIMACY
Based on Chapter 7 of *A House that Grace Built*

Our closest family relationships are meant to provide a reservoir where we can be loved, known, heard, and validated. It is through these relationships where we are meant to form a "home base"—a place of safety and security that allows shelter from life's outside storms. Through these relationship, the essential lifetime bonds of closeness and security are meant to be formed.

Marriage was created to be the deepest form of human intimacy. Marriage, in fact, is meant to model the deep level of intimacy God desires to establish in our relationship with Him.

The role of a parent is also created to house a deep form of intimate interactions. As a parent, we are given the opportunity to teach our children how to love and be intimate in future relationships as well.

Based on the purpose of these relationships, it should be obvious how damaging and destructive it can be when their purposes are contaminated, displaced, or neglected. Rather than reflect the design of intimacy for which they were created, we can be injured and wounded in profound and compelling ways.

Chapter Highlights
- Intimacy in marriage
- Being single
- Intimacy as parents

Homework Purpose
In this chapter, we want to continue through an assessment process, this time focusing on the sacred roles of marriage and parenting. If we are not married or do not have children, this is still a very useful exercise. It can prepare us for future relationships, equip us to understand the issues of those around us, or better help us learn from our upbringing. Identifying and diagnosing is always necessary before applying an actual remedy. In later chapters (Chapter 12 and 13), we'll specifically deal with these relationships for the sole purpose of restoring, redeeming or healing from any damage that may have been imposed.

ASSESSING INTIMACY IN MARRIAGE

Learning to view our own intimacy style in marriage is helpful in addressing the areas that need to be healed. If these are issues that have occurred in the past, it's important that we see and comprehend them. If we do not currently have a spouse, we can see how intimacy was modeled through our own parental experience, thus disposing us to various intimacy styles that may appear in our present or future relationships.

ASSESSING SPIRITUAL INTIMACY IN MARRIAGE

Does your marriage (past, present, or parental example) contain spiritual intimacy? If spiritual intimacy is lacking, can you identify the source?

_____

_____

_____

If you are unequally yoked with a spouse, how have you tried to deal with the lack of spiritual resources in the relationship?

_____

_____

_____

What's your best weapon to deal with an unequally yoked situation?

_____

_____

_____

MENTAL INTIMACY IN MARRIAGE

How have you (past, present, or through observation of parents) learned to connect intimately to a spouse through your thoughts and communication?

_____

_____

_____

Is (or was) there honest dialogue in your marriage? Why or why not?

_____

_____

_____

INTIMACY IN THE WILL IN MARRIAGE

Describe how you are bonded through the choices you make in your marriage?

_____

_____

_____

Is (was) compliance based on godly submission, or elements of unhealthy control?

_____

_____

_____

EMOTIONAL INTIMACY IN MARRIAGE

Describe how feelings are (were) dealt with in your marriage relationship.

_____

_____

_____

Is it safe to feel authentically, or do you hide, repress, or express hurt indirectly (such as anger or rage)?

_____

_____

_____

Can you share your feelings with your spouse? Can he/she share feelings with you?

_____

_____

_____

Have you ever had an emotional affair outside the marriage or recognized that your spouse had one? Describe the dynamics relating to that.

_____

_____

_____

SEXUAL INTIMACY IN MARRIAGE

Can you identify with any sexual intimacy issues in marriage?

_____

_____

_____

Are you aware of anything that has occurred outside of the marriage that would make sexual intimacy difficult, painful, or disinteresting?

_____

_____

_____

A WORD TO SINGLES

When we are single, we are given special access to the Lord as our Husband. We can share a relationship free from the constraints and pressures of earthly marriage. While marriage is God's plan in many of our lives, it may or may not be God's in our own. Learning to embrace singleness can be a journey. And for some of us, it is temporary and a preparation for marriage in the future. In either case, we want to have our perceptions of being single cleansed and purified, so God can have access to our hearts and lives either way.

What is your current attitude towards being single? Do you feel comfortable or uncomfortable with your status? Have you reached a point in your singlehood where having Jesus Christ as your Husband is satisfying, or is there still a deep ache for a human spouse? What can you do to use your singleness as a gift, rather than feel deprived by it?

_____

_____

_____

If you desire marriage, list the number one area you have realized needs to be worked on to prepare you for marriage in the future.

_____

_____

_____

INTIMACY IN PARENTING

Parenting requires an extreme form of giving, where our ability to bond with our children will deeply affect their own growth and development. The styles and patterns we bring to this room are not set in stone and have the ability, as with all other relationships, to be changed. If we recognize a distortion, it gives us the opportunity to allow God to cleanse and restore our role (see Chapter 13).

Can you recognize any distortions in your intimacy styles as a parent? Can you see the connection to the issues you brought into adulthood?

_____

_____

_____

Are you dealing with any specific circumstances that require intervention as a parent? If so, list the need and add it to your journal.

_____

_____

_____

CHAPTER 8
ASSESSING INTIMACY IN OUR COURTS

Based on Chapter 8 of *A House that Grace Built*

As we've learned in previous chapters, the inner courts of our lives represent God's design for close connection. In addition to these areas, we can have many relationships that fall outside the designation of intimacy. In fact, as we leave our homes each day, we prepare to interact and mingle within the "outer courts" of our lives. These are places where we participate in relationships with people who don't know the inside workings of our hearts and lives. Instead, these relationships are designed to be kept strictly at a guest level where we can interact, but not necessarily allow people inside.

Our friendships and relationships to people, places and things will manifest in different ways. But we can be assured when we are overly motivated to find intimacy in unhealthy ways in our outer court, it always indicates there is something on inside needs to dealt with.

Chapter Highlights
- Intimacy in friendships
- Intimacy with activities
- Intimacy with things
- Assessing our courts

Homework Purpose

By understanding how relationship patterns are rooted in the inner court, we will be able to see how our outer courts have also been affected. In this chapter, we will also assess different dysfunctional intimacy styles that occur when we have displaced intimacy needs. We will highlight each one and begin to see the correlation between them. Finally, we will chart our own intimacy styles. This will help to take what has been revealed, and visually display it for our own insight and clarity.

INTIMACY IN FRIENDSHIPS

Our friends are meant to be an outside resource to assist and support us in our family roles, our work, our ministries, and other aspects of our lives. They are not meant to entirely replace God-ordained intimate roles, such as a marriage partner. Yet they can certainly offer us the gift of closeness and acceptance that sometimes can be missing or invalidated in our family lives.

We can have friendships that are rooted in our inner courts, but many of our friendships throughout our lifetimes will be more casual. Understanding the roles we place on our friendships is significant. Furthermore, recognizing how we embrace intimacy patterns in friendships will help us see our own areas of vulnerability.

Can you recognize any unhealthy patterns in your friendship styles? For instance, are you using friendships to replace the intimacy needs that aren't being met elsewhere? Or do you push friendships away out of fear of intimacy?

_____

_____

_____

INTIMACY WITH ACTIVITY

Filling our lives up with busy activities can be a method used to deal with a sense of disconnect and loneliness in our human relationships. We can try to focus on what we need "to do," in order to avoid facing the deeper relational problems. Focusing on our work is one example of this distortion.

Describe your relationship to activities. Can you see where you are prone to use activity to deal with a missing, invalidated, or broken intimacy need?

_____

_____

_____

INTIMACY WITH THINGS

God is the Giver of all gifts. He provides many things based on our needs and our pleasure. But since things do not contain spirit life or provide the ability to emotionally connect, things are not intended to replace the human connection designated in our hearts. Therefore, when we place a high value on "things," we can unknowingly attempt to use material goods to fill our inward needs.

Describe your relationship to things. Can you see where you are prone to use things to deal with a missing, invalidated, or broken intimacy need?

_____

_____

ASSESSING OUR COURTS

Evaluating our own courts is important. Even if we feel unsure on how our intimacy styles have appeared, by actually writing them down and praying over them, God can begin to shed light. Remember, the process of assessment takes on a diagnostic purpose. God does not highlight anything dysfunctional to hurt us, but rather to heal us.

GOD'S DESIGN FOR INTIMACY

Refer to the charts on page 54 . The chart on God's design for intimacy highlights the order God intended for our intimacy charts.

MY CURRENT INTIMACY

Refer to the chart on page 55. On this chart, write all the names of your relationships in the order that they are right now. Be totally honest and prayerfully assess the proper location for each. To assist you, let's evaluate each area:

Holy of Holies

Is there anything competing with the space that only is intended for God to fill through Jesus Christ? Include anything you've recognized as an idol in your heart. If God has honestly not been given access into the Holy of Holies, write His name in the other part of your heart where you've kept His placement.

_____
_____
_____

Inner Court

Are the people God intended to be intimately close to you in that area of your heart?

_____
_____
_____

If they are not, can you identify some reasons why those relationships lack intimacy?

_____
_____
_____

How has a lack of intimacy in close relationships affected other intimacy patterns in your life?

_____

_____

Are there any patterns of allowing people into your inner court who do not belong? Explain.

_____

_____

_____

Are other people, things, or activities used in your life to deal with a lack of healthy intimate connections?

_____

_____

_____

Outer Court
Explain how you interact in your outer courts.

_____

_____

_____

In general, what is your criteria for allowing people to see into your heart?

_____

_____

_____

Do you ever feel that your outer court doesn't reflect the truth of who you are? Explain.

_____

_____

_____

My Desired Intimacy
Refer to the chart on page 56. Write how you desire the positions of intimacy to be given. In other words, if you could have the relationships set to the preference of closeness, who would be on the

chart and how would the chart appear?

IDENTIFYING BROKEN INTIMACY
Action Step
1. Write the names of people (God included if applicable) with whom your relationship has suffered because of broken intimacy and then fill out the worksheet (page 57) for each person (use separate paper if necessary).
2. Be sure to include these issues that are revealed somewhere in your journal.

A Prayer for Broken Intimacy
Lord God,

As I look at the rooms of my heart, I acknowledge that some of my relationships have been broken. Whether by my choice or theirs, the sin and messiness of life has stolen away something that You designed to be precious. Father, I acknowledge that I allowed people into my heart who didn't belong. Other times, I kept people out who did belong. I pray that You would clean, heal, and prepare each room in my heart for Your perfect plan. If You can restore my relationships, I pray that You would help me and the people in my life deal with broken intimacy needs. I pray that You would work in both of our hearts. If You require me to release and grieve this relationship, prepare my heart to do just that, so I can move on in a healthy way and allow the other spaces to be filled as You intended.

In Jesus's name. Amen.

UNHEALTHY INTIMACY STYLES
Describe the specific ways you can recognize your intimacy style has been broken based on what you learned in these past four chapters.

_____

_____

_____

_____

_____

_____

_____

_____

_____

_____

God's Design for Intimacy Levels

Inner Court

Holy of Holies
Sanctuary reserved for God. Manifests His presence

Parents Intimacy changes

Siblings Intimacy changes

Other family

Close friend

Children (after spouse next intimate)

Spouse Most intimate

Outer Courts
Friendships
Acquaintances
Ministry
Work

Gateway to my soul → Allows or inhibits access based on God's wisdom and discernment

My Current Intimacy

Outer Courts
Who stays outside in the outer courts, even if they are meant by God to be inside?

Who is intimately close in my soul?

Inner Court

Holy of Holies
Who or what consumes my affection?

Gateway to my soul
- Do I allow people in too much, or not allow at all?
- Have I forged an additional wall of protection?

List the important relationships in your life and the area they are located.

Write HONESTLY how they are right at this moment, even if you can acknowledge it is faulty.

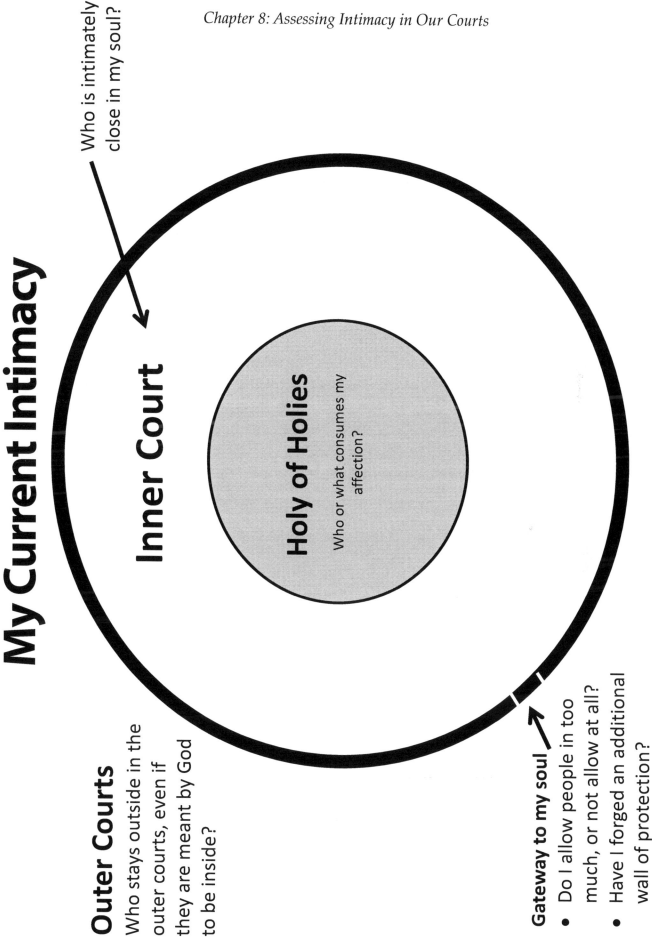

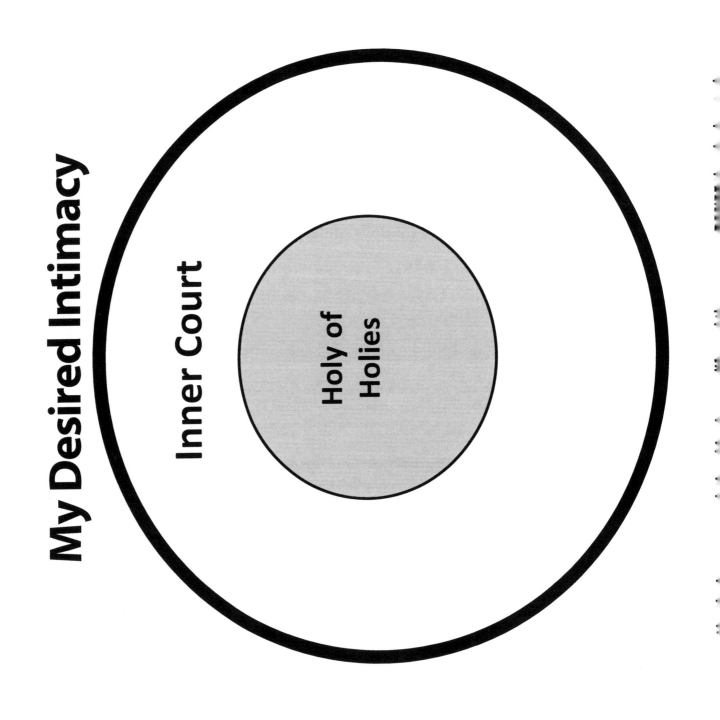

My Desired Intimacy

Outer Courts

Inner Court

Holy of Holies

ASSESSING INTIMACY WORKSHEET

Name of Person: _____

God-ordained role: _____

Does that relationship align with God's design? Why or why not?

_____

_____

_____

What is your method style of intimacy with this person? (What do you do or not do to display intimacy?)

_____

_____

_____

What do you think inhibits you from being intimate?

_____

_____

_____

What is _____ intimacy style with you?

_____

_____

_____

What do you think blocks their ability from being intimate with you (if applicable)?

_____

_____

_____

Can you see anything specifically that has interfered with intimacy?

_____

_____

CHAPTER 9
THE DOORWAY OF REDEMPTION

Based on Chapter 9 of *A House that Grace Built*

God is a Redeemer! He doesn't leave us in our brokenness, but gives us tools and resources to learn to align our relationship skills with Him. Our codependence consisted of a set of improper coping methods to deal with relationship problems. Thus, we typically believed that if we did something, said something, or responded appropriately in that relationship, we could turn the situation around. In fact, the very essence of our codependence was the belief that we *did* have the power to change a person; thus, we were driven to "try harder." But this merry-go-round of codependence insanity only caused the root of rejection to deepen and a sense of hopelessness to emerge.

Throughout the next five chapters, we are digging deep into the redemptive principles of God, seeking to filter the "rooms of our hearts" through His point of view, not necessarily our own. This means it is imperative that we connect the redemption process with the movements of the Spirit of God, thus we cease operating from our own effort and self-sufficiency.

Chapter Highlights
- God's love and holiness
- Holiness and grace
- Accessing holiness

Homework Purpose

This first chapter under "redemption" is heavily biblical so that we can gain revelation into the process God provides for our redemption. In Chapter 10 we will break this down into more practical application. But before the practical side of recovery has any value, we must first connect this process to God's heart and His ways. Understanding the Old Testament and the system of the law is incredibly important to understanding the overall bondage of codependence. In additional, understanding the power of grace will single-handedly change our entire lives and move us into the freedom of God.

OUR POINT OF VIEW

Learning how we dealt with the relationships up to this point is helpful. It will reflect our general belief system of how the people in our life can changed. Answer the following:

What have you defined as the critical relationship needs in your life?

_____

_____

_____

How have you handled each one up until this point?

_____

_____

_____

Are you willing to allow God to take over the relationship and assert His remedy into the situation, even though it might be uncomfortable at first? If not, what is keeping you back?

_____

_____

_____

UNDERSTANDING GOD'S HOLINESS AND LOVE

We typically fail to understand significant aspects of God's character. Oftentimes, we don't truly grasp the nature of God's love towards us. But just the same, we don't understand the reality of His holy nature. In order to begin to assess our understanding through God's principles, we are going to take an in-depth look at how we interpret holiness.

Explain your understanding of God's holiness and love.

_____

_____

_____

Can you identify where you might overly emphasize one aspect, while negate the other? Explain.

_____

_____

_____

ACCESSING HOLINESS AND GRACE

In authentic Christian living, we must embrace the reality that holiness isn't something we earn through our own merit or effort; it is a direct result of grace working its way through us. In fact, the transaction of the blood of Jesus Christ holds all the power necessary to redeem and restore our hearts. Therefore, we must never think for a moment that we can do it without Him.

How have you interpreted holiness?

_____

_____

_____

Did you feel responsible for your own sense of holiness?

_____

_____

_____

How did you think God felt about the areas in your life that weren't right? How has that perspective changed?

_____

_____

_____

GAINING HOLINESS

Since holiness is something God does in us, learning how to gain holiness in a real way can be perplexing. Yet the Word of God offers us many insightful truths that can aid and direct us. We learned in Chapter 9 about Isaiah's encounter with God. While this Scripture may seem too far removed from our own experiences, it in fact lays the framework of how God desires to interact with us. Like Isaiah, God will make us aware of our defects and sin to initiate the process of true repentance. Through this state of contrition, we are purged and purified.

Action Step

To put this in perspective, we are going to revisit a concept introduced in Chapter 9. Once again, imagine standing in the physical temple of the Old Testament—walking through the veil and entering into the Holy of Holies. Take some time to close your eyes and meditate.

Once you can visualize yourself being in the presence of God's holiness—picture yourself being stripped down and spiritually naked before Him. Now, answer the following questions: How do you see yourself before Him—with everything exposed and open? Do you feel shame? Do you feel accepted?

_____

_____

_____

What do you think God sees and feels? Are His eyes angry at you? Disappointed? Loving? Compassionate? Do you feel acceptance or rejection? Be honest in your answer—not what you should say, but what you truly do feel.

_____

_____

_____

Now, picture a robe or coat being draped over you; it reflects the most awesome and glorious condition of purity and beauty. This is the righteousness of Christ. It's what we receive when we strip off our own self-survival and self-righteousness and come to God as we are. This is how He is allowed into the Holy of Holies within our bodily temple and fills our deepest and most sacred reservoir of intimacy. It's the indwelling of the Spirit of God—the place where you can meet with and partake of the glory of God.

Have you reached a place where you can honestly say that God's exposure of your unholiness brings the blessed reality of His grace covering you? Do you struggle with understanding this?

_____

_____

_____

These principles encompass an overview that will be further broken down in specific ways in chapters to come. Thus, they provide some definitions that will be reiterated throughout the workbook.

Describe your own experience with meeting God. Have you felt both His holiness and love? Have you met with grace? If not, what is holding you back?

_____

_____

_____

CHAPTER 10
APPLYING REDEMPTIVE PRINCIPLES

Based on Chapter 10 of *A House that Grace Built*

Learning key spiritual principles is the beginning towards freedom, but actually being able to apply them will assure us that God's truth can be a reality in our lives. Understanding the theology behind God's plan and provision for our lives doesn't guarantee that we are walking and living in it. Thus, we need to learn to translate God's perspective into our daily experience. Because God's agenda is redemption, as we become willing to face the relational challenges in our lives, we will need to understand that He is working to re-align those relationships using His strategies. In Chapter 10 we looked at three ways God wants to deal with our relationships:

1. Apply the filter of redemption to our relationships
2. Understand the spiritual design of relationships
3. Embrace God's order in relationships

Chapter Highlights

- Applying redemption to relationships
- Spiritual design of relationships
- God's order in relationships

Homework Purpose

This application project will help us to understand each concept contained in the redemptive process, as well as key in on areas of vulnerability. These principles encompass an overview that will be further broken down in specific ways in chapters to come. Thus, they provide some definitions that will be reiterated throughout the workbook.

APPLYING REDEMPTION TO RELATIONSHIPS

In Chapter 10 we took the spiritual process of Chapter 9 and broke it into practical ways we can initiate redemption in relationships. Let's address each one.

1. ***We must face the truth of each relationship, not allowing denial to blind us.***
Where has truth begun to help you walk in freedom?

_____

_____

_____

Can you explain where or how you resist the truth of your relationships?

_____

_____

_____

2. ***We must operate by vulnerability more than self-protection.***
Are you more prone to self-protect than expose your true self?

_____

_____

_____

Are there relationships where your authenticity before God and others would be beneficial?

_____

_____

_____

Explain those relationships where you are cautious about being vulnerable and the reason for it.

_____

_____

_____

3. ***We must cease any form of control.***
Do you have any relationships that continue to operate from control?

_____

_____

_____

Explain how control plays out in relationships, describing the effect.

_____

_____

_____

4. *We must detach in love.*

Do you have any relationships where unhealthy enmeshment has occurred, or patterns have evolved that are difficult to break?

_____

_____

_____

How can you detach in love without throwing a person away?

_____

_____

_____

5. *We must cleanse each room.*

We will be proceeding with this process in the next few chapters. Describe any rooms that God has revealed need cleansing.

_____

_____

_____

6. *We must authentically grieve.*

There is no specific way to initiate the process of grieving, other than a readiness to allow God to lead us into it. We learned about grief in Chapter 2, and we need to continually allow for opportunities where it can be implemented as God directs us.

_____

_____

_____

7. *We must be willing to reconnect.*

Disconnection is never God's purpose in our relationships. What God wants to teach us is when and where we are to initiate methods to reconcile or take action in our relationships.

List the relationship where reconnection is needed.

_____

_____

_____

8. *We have opportunity to intercede.*
List those people in your life who you want to pray over.

_____

_____

_____

9. *We must love others as God loves us.*
Do you enter into relationships expecting people to have the ability to love you properly, even though they haven't yet received the tools?

_____

_____

_____

How have you handled it in the past? How can you handle it today?

_____

_____

_____

10. *Set reasonable expectations.*
We will address this in detail in Chapter 17.

GOD'S SPIRITUAL DESIGN FOR RELATIONSHIPS

The relationship roles we have in our lifetimes are not random. They have been created by God to reflect a different aspect of His heart and character towards us. Usually, we are unaware of this reality. Thus, it is important that we learn to see the relational design as God intended it to be. From there, we can begin to work through the brokenness we may have experienced in that earthly role.

Have you ever considered how your earthly relationships are meant to reflect an aspect of God's character? Can you see God as Father, Husband, Brother and Friend?

_____

_____

_____

Can you see how the distortion of your earthly relationships may have affected your interpretation of God? Explain.

_____

_____

_____

GOD'S ORDER IN RELATIONSHIPS

Learning how God ordered relationships is important. However, the most important aspect of being re-aligned in relationship with Him is to place our lives under God's authority. From there, we have the resources necessary to learn to function in our earthly roles.

By claiming the authority of Jesus Christ, we are empowered to deal with everything in our lives that has been broken or injured. That's because the voice of God by default outweighs the voice of any human being.

Have you reinstated God's authority? Are you confident that He is above anything in your life that has ever caused pain or damage to you?

_____

_____

_____

How do you deal with your earthly authority?

_____

_____

_____

CHAPTER 11
CLOSING THE ROOMS OF THE PAST
Based on Chapter 11 of *A House that Grace Built*

Throughout the process contained in *TCCRW: From Surviving to Significance* and the process in *A House that Grace Built*, we have been brought in touch with a variety of issues stemming from our early life experiences. While we have addressed these issues in a variety of ways, as we seek to open up and personalize each room in our hearts, it's important that we don't lump the "past" into one general compartment.

That's why for the next several chapters we will be asked to look at specific relationships, with specific people. Our ability to do this will assure that we deal with the rooms that have not yet been properly cleansed, and are therefore affecting us in unhealthy ways.

In this chapter we focused on the impacting relationships of our childhood and early adulthood. Even though we may have already worked through these relationships in other ways, this chapter will help assure us that we have properly addressed each need and can leave the room in a cleansed state.

Chapter Highlights
- Cleansing early childhood rooms: parents, siblings, friends
- Cleansing early adulthood: dating, friends and attachment styles

Homework Purpose
As we repeatedly learned, assessing and understanding our past is not meant to place blame on the people who may have hurt us. Instead, it's meant to purify and cleanse our own heart.

In this application process, we will dig deep into assessing our individual situations, preparing for God to restore and cleanse each relationship according to His purposes. We enter into the rooms of our past no longer equipped with our weapons of self defense. Rather, we come covered in the grace and authority of Jesus Christ.

Assessing Early Childhood Relationships

In this chapter we reviewed several relationships from our early childhood experience that may be in need of cleansing. Even if we feel that we have already worked through the issues surrounding that relationship, it is recommended that we run the cleansing process through them nonetheless. For some of us, that relational room may be in need of extensive cleansing; but for others of us, we may only need a slight "dusting" or "vacuuming." In order to assess each room, use the worksheet listed on Page 72.

Applying Redemption (cleansing the room - childhood)

Taking note of how a relational rooms needs to be cleaned equips us to understand how to deal with each need that is exposed. The power of forgiveness acts as the actual cleansing agent when it is done in the context of truth and through the Holy Spirit (not emotional sentiment).

Actions Steps

1. Visualize taking that person into the Holy of Holies and presenting that person before the Lord.
2. Ask God to cover that person with the blood of Jesus Christ—and to provide him or her with the full provision of forgiveness and redemption. (Please note, if anger or resentments appear to be a challenge, please go through Chapter 9 of *TCCRW: From Surviving to Significance* to review the process of forgiveness in detail.)

Renounce

When we renounce something, we are essentially "kicking it out" and denying it access in the future. If we had an unwanted guest in our home, for example, we would ask them to leave and then make sure they didn't return. In our relationships, we don't renounce actual people necessarily. Instead, we renounce harmful behaviors and faulty messages that were sent into our lives. We can also renounce the spiritual influence behind the wrongful actions committed against us (or we committed against someone). Remember, anything that is based on a lie or seeks to hurt, steal or destroy our lives comes from the Enemy. That doesn't indicate the people in our lives are demonic, it simply means that Satan attempted to use their brokenness or weakness to hurt us (or used our brokenness or weakness to hurt them).

Action Steps

1. Speak against and renounce the sin and harmful messages that were sent through the relationship using the authority of Jesus Christ. For example, "I renounce _____ (list the behavior) and the message it sent into my life."
2. Announce the truth of God that replaces that lie. For example, "I am a child of the Living God, and I am pure and holy in His sight."
3. Spiritually close the door for relationships that exist in the past, not necessarily in the present. Command any spiritual influence other than the Holy Spirit to leave in Jesus name.

4. Ask God to direct how far to open or close the door in the present relationship if applicable.
5. Pray for that door to not be opened in a harmful or negative way ever again, severing any unhealthy soul ties, but preserving its space for God's plan and purposes.

GRIEVE

Especially where death, separation, violation, or neglect has occurred, grief is the most important key of truly being able to heal and move on (Refer to Chapter 2). Grief oftentimes will appear once the actual cleansing has taken place.

EARLY ADULTHOOD

In early adulthood patterns begin to emerge based on our choices. When we are children, often we are unable to make choices because someone makes them on our behalf. This phase of our life therefore reflects how we engage in relationships, and specifically what we allow or disallow in each relationship. To assess this, let's look at the following:

What unhealthy patterns of dating emerged in early adulthood? Describe.

_____

_____

_____

Pinpoint your attachment styles early in adulthood. Did you overly attach to people? Did you depend on yourself and not trust people at all? Explain.

_____

_____

_____

Describe the patterns that emerged as you learned how to work, pursue dreams, or raise a family. Did you make healthy choices, or did you wind up with the effects of something based on unhealthy choices?

_____

_____

_____

Describe the key events that took place in your early adulthood life that may have had a negative influence on your life today?

_____

_____

_____

CLEANSING THE ROOM WORKSHEET - EARLY CHILDHOOD

If working through childhood, list the names of every significant inner court relationship (mom, dad, sibling, etc.)

_____

_____

_____

Answer the following (use separate paper if necessary):
What overall memories come to mind when you consider that person? Are they positive or negative?

_____

_____

_____

What do you remember feeling the most inside that childhood room with that person?

_____

_____

_____

Did this person have commit violations against you that still harm you today? How?

_____

_____

_____

Did you commit violations against this person?

_____

_____

_____

What weapons did you bring with you to deal with the difficulties that room contained (control, denial, fear)?

_____

_____

_____

Up until now, has the room been cleansed? (If the room is cleaned from previous recovery and spiritual experiences, it is unnecessary to continue. But if there is even a small possibility that there's something left inside, it's best to continue.) _____ Yes _____No

APPLYING REDEMPTION (CLEANSING THE ROOM - ADULTHOOD)

Actions Steps

1. Write the name of each relationship within the room that affected you in your early adulthood. If your relationships with your parents, family, or certain friends were particularly important, include them in the context of early adulthood (even if you listed them in childhood or have a relationship with them today).

2. Follow the previous process used in the childhood rooms. Use the worksheet on page 74. If you need assistance with recovering memories or connecting to the emotions of an event, you can:

    a. Write a story about what happened and focus primarily on what you felt as a result of that person's behaviors. This helps to attempt to recall that memory and bring it to the forefront. Before writing, pray and ask God to assist you with retrieving important memories.

    b. Write letters to the people involved, forgiving them for what they did wrong.

3. If you feel that you are still affected by guilt and shame, bring yourself into the Holy of Holies and claim the blood of Jesus as all sufficient to authoritatively dominate your heart. Believe that the cross has conquered and redeemed each and every mistake that was ever made.

CLEANSING THE ROOM WORKSHEET - EARLY ADULTHOOD

List the names of every significant inner court relationship
(boyfriend, girlfriend, friend, spouse, etc.)

_____

_____

_____

Answer the following (use separate paper if necessary):
What overall memories come to mind when you consider that person? Are they positive or negative?

_____

_____

_____

What do you remember feeling the most inside that childhood room with that person?

_____

_____

_____

Did this person have commit violations against you that still harm you today? How?

_____

_____

_____

Did you commit violations against this person?

_____

_____

_____

What weapons did you bring with you to deal with the difficulties that room contained (control, denial, fear)?

_____

_____

_____

Up until now, has the room been cleansed? (If the room is cleaned from previous recovery and spiritual experiences, it is unnecessary to continue. But if there is even a small possibility that there's something left inside, it's best to continue.) _____ Yes _____No

CHAPTER 12
CLEANSING THE ROOM OF MARRIAGE

Based on Chapter 12 of *A House that Grace Built*

What we carry into adulthood from past relationships will often deeply affect our choices and ability to relate in our roles within marriage and parenting. Furthermore, because marriage is the most intimate relationship created by God, when it doesn't function as He intended, it can sabotage our understanding of His plan. In fact, apart from His spiritual overlay, marriage will lose its foundational purposes.

In this next chapter, we will take a direct look at the important components of marriage, and how they align and represent God's own heart. This will give us the ability to identify the spiritual roots that require God's intervention. Furthermore, we can look at how God intends to restore and redeem our marriage rooms. For some of us, we can't participate in this with a spouse. We must understand that we can cleanse this room despite the participation of our spouse past or present. For others of us, we are ready to apply the tools that will help navigate a redemptive process in our marriage. This application project will offer you some basic insight as how to heal a marriage.

Chapter Highlights

- Assessing marriage
- Redeeming marriage in our heart
- Redeeming marriage with each other
- Divorce and singlehood

Homework Purpose

This chapter entails an intensive process of working through our marital issues, past or present. The reason this chapter includes such detail is that it is the very deepest place in our hearts (beside the Holy of Holies). We must at some point be willing to face this comprehensively to evaluate what is happening in that room of our heart.

For those of who aren't married, we can understand the intricate details of marriage to prepare in the future. We can also see patterns emerge through the dating styles we acquired until now.

ASSESSING THE MARRIAGE ROOM

In order to understand the purpose of marriage, we must see it through the filter of its God-given design. Marriage wasn't merely meant to make us happy, it was created to reflect the nature and attributes of how God is married to us. Therefore, all its attributes are meant to mimic God's intimacy style. Let's look at some of the key areas where we can see the marriage room through God's heart.

MARRIAGE AND LOVE

The love God created for marriage was intended to stand the test of time and circumstances. That's because its cohesive element was intended to be held by His Spirit, not mere human sentiment. As we learned in Chapter 12, a lack of love for our spouses is actually a spiritual condition, not an emotional or human problem. That doesn't negate that our relationships can undergo significant challenges, but love by its very nature and definition is not reliant on a person, but is dependent on the resource of God Himself.

If you are married or were married in the past, describe how love is/was operating. What can you pinpoint as the cause for love's breakdown?

_____
_____
_____

How have you dealt with a lack of love? How do you try to gain love from your spouse?

_____
_____
_____

SINGLENESS OF HEART

Just as God requires a set-apart affection for Him above anyone or anything else, so was the marriage relationship created to represent this level of exclusivity. While marriage is never meant to replace God's position, it is meant to rise above all other earthly relationships in its priority and designation.

In your own marriage (past, present, or parental modeling) can you identify a breach in singleness of heart?

_____
_____
_____

If you were on the receiving side of this, explain how that affected you?

_____
_____

If you were not able to give singleness of heart, describe the reasons for this.

_____

_____

_____

BECOMING HOLY

Most often we entered into close relationships wanting to find happiness. In a marriage, we can carry this ideal as the central goal of its success. Yet through God's perspective, happiness is never His agenda in and of itself. While God certainly wants to bless us and fill us with peace, He desires that our lives are purified, and we are brought to wholeness.

The marriage relationship has a special purpose in assisting us in the process of sanctification. It helps us see our weaknesses and defects at deeper levels than any other relationship; thus, it can promote an environment where we can be more and more purified. Yet more often than not, the issues that arise in a marriage are what lead to division, conflict, and separation.

Do you see how God is using marriage to make you more holy?

_____

_____

_____

How does your spouse deal with your imperfections?

_____

_____

_____

How do you deal with his or her imperfections?

_____

_____

_____

WALKING BY GRACE

In creating an environment of growth, God takes our brokenness and transforms it by His grace. That means where we are weak, He becomes our strength. God's love allows us to see what we can't do or how we can't live apart from Him.

In marriage, grace is the only remedy to deal with the problems that arise. God's grace operates through humility and repentance; therefore, when we are dealing with an unrepentant person, boundaries are required.

A true successful marriage will not emerge by two people perfectly performing their roles, but by both spouses receiving and offering grace in everyday situations.

Do you see grace in your relationship? If not, what is hindering or damaging it?

_____

_____

_____

What does your spouse need spiritually right now? How have you tried to deal with that need?

_____

_____

_____

What can you do right now? What should you not attempt to do with the problems or deficiencies of your spouse?

_____

_____

_____

TRUST

Trust is conditional. We can trust someone to the extent that they have proved trustworthy. When trust is shattered, it can bring devastating effects. For some of us, history and behaviors have brought distrust into marriage. For others, we brought our own inabilities to trust into marriage; therefore, trust was hindered regardless of what our spouses did or didn't do. It's important that we recognize and see our own trust issues.

How is trust in operation within your marriage?

_____

_____

_____

Do you trust your spouse?

_____

_____

_____

Does your spouse trust you?

_____

_____

_____

If trust has been breached, describe what you think caused this to occur?

_____

_____

_____

APPLYING REDEMPTION TO MARRIAGE

In this next section, we'll look at what we can do through redemptive principles to deal with the areas in our marriages that aren't working as God intended. Because we may be dealing with a past spouse, or a current spouse who isn't participating in recovery, we need to first apply these principles to our own hearts.

Under each heading, two principles will be given. The first says "What Can I Do Now?" This is referring to our own level of responsibility in the marriage, and is NOT reliant upon how our spouses react or respond to us. Then, there is another principle that says "What Can We Do Together?" If we are in situations where our spouses are actively pursuing healing and we are ready to commit to growing and healing together, this section offers some ways that can happen. It is NOT recommended doing the "together" part until each spouse has first completed the "What Can I Do Now?" project. Let's look at each.

FACING TRUTH

In cleansing the rooms of our hearts, we must get in touch with the truth that has been revealed about them.

What Can I Do Now?
Assess the weaknesses and strengths in your own marriage. Answer the following:
What were my expectations coming into marriage?

_____

_____

_____

How were those expectations not realized?

_____

_____

_____

How do I see my spouse in marriage right now?

_____

_____

_____

How do I think my spouse sees me?

_____

_____

_____

What are my spouse's greatest failures and weaknesses in the marriage?

_____

_____

_____

What are my greatest failures and weaknesses in the marriage?

_____

_____

_____

How is love operating in my marriage?

_____

_____

_____

How is shame operating in my marriage?

_____

_____

_____

What is my dream and hope for my marriage?

_____

_____

_____

What Can We Do Together?

In preparing ourselves for a process of reconciliation with our spouse, we will at some point need to be able to work through a truth-telling project together. An example of a truth-telling project can be found on page 82. If God directs, we can even share our answers we wrote in "What Can I Do Now?"

VULNERABILITY

When we've been hurt by a spouse, we can begin to self-protect in a variety of ways. While sometimes boundaries may be necessary, other times self-protection inhibits the ability to experience any form of intimacy.

What Can I Do Now?
Look for the reasons you have begun to self-protect in marriage.

_____

_____

_____

What do you fear most? Is there a better way to deal with these issues?

_____

_____

_____

List the behaviors that cause you to fear, hide, or detach from your spouse.

_____

_____

_____

Once the list is complete, take that list, and say the following:

When you (speak the behavior that was listed), I feel _____ (write an emotion).

What is the primary emotion you have unmasked? How can you better deal with that?

_____

_____

_____

What Can We Do Together?

Begin to write lists of the deeper feelings and needs you haven't been able to express in the past. But this time, share them with your spouse. When doing this, DO NOT emphasize your spouse's behaviors or mistakes; just focus on your personal emotions.

When two people learn to do this in a healthy manner, sharing these vulnerable truths will bring understanding and connection (We cannot do this unless both people in the marriage have gone through some level of individual healing.).

TRUTH TELLING EXERCISE

Strongholds get implanted in marriage relationships by repetitive beliefs that we impose on each other. The purpose of this worksheet it to identify those beliefs, both positive and negative. This can only work if you are completely honest. Tell what's in your heart, not what you think your partner wants to hear, etc.

When I look at you, I see _____

When you look at me, I think you see _____

One of the things I love most about you is_____

I feel most loved by you when _____

I feel closest and most intimate (physically, spiritually, or emotionally) with you when

_____

I wish you understood this about me _____

I wish you'd respect that I _____

I wish you'd appreciate me when I_____

What I need the most from you is _____

The thing that feels most neglected in our relationship is _____

Of anything I've done wrong, I wish you could forgive me for _____

Of my hang-ups and quirks, I wish you would accept this _____

What hurts me most is when you _____

I am afraid when you _____

You let me down when _____

I get angry when _____

I am insecure when _____

When you get angry at me I feel_____

When I know I let you down or hurt you I feel _____

My deepest dream about our relationship would be

_____

I hope we can experience more physical, emotional, and spiritual intimacy.

Physically_____

Emotionally_____

Spiritually _____

I admit that I need to work on myself in this way _____

_____

I am giving this you because I desire to share honestly what is inside my heart. Please give me time, grace, and space to deal with my own issues. I will stop attempting to focus on your shortcomings because I realize that I contribute. Please pray for me, and I will pray for you.

CONTROL

Wherever we are attempting to manipulate the outcomes of our marriages, or find ways to make our spouses change, we are engaged in controlling behaviors. When both spouses mutually control each other, the relationship takes on a deep form of bondage, opposing the principles of freedom by which authentic love is designed to flow.

What Can I Do Now?

Ask God if you have surrendered your marriage and spouse to Him, ceasing all forms of your own control.

_____

_____

_____

If you have not surrendered your marriage to God, what keeps you back?

_____

_____

_____

Can you identify a particular method of control that you continue to use?

_____

_____

_____

What Can We Do Together?

In reconciling a marriage, two spouses must be willing to surrender control and stand under the submission of God first and foremost. A husband who submits to God will love His wife and care for her needs. A wife who submits to God will have the ability to submit to her husband. Both spouses are accountable to God first and then to their respective roles.

Surrendering to God and submitting to each other is the beautiful key to a healthy marriage. There is no direct project we can do to make this happen other than pray together and stay willing and humble.

DETACH IN LOVE

Detaching can happen through different seasons of marriage where we commit to work on ourselves. It is not meant to be a long-term relationship style unless there are significant reasons or problems. Detaching allows us to cut ourselves out as separate people in our relationships to God and to our spouses. It is not meant to be mistaken as separation or departure of the relationship.

Have you been able to detach in marriage in your healing process to gain a better perspective? Describe.

_____

_____

_____

What can you do right to initiate that process?

_____

_____

_____

What Can We Do Together?

While a healthy marriage should be formed upon intimacy with each other, both spouses need to understand that their relationship to God is primary. Therefore, it may be healthy to agree upon days or times where there is a willingness to retreat and spend time on spiritual reflection before God.

Action Steps

After designating "together" time to bond and grow spiritually, both spouses can find some designated "me" time. This includes:

1. Time for personal devotion and prayer
2. Time with healthy friendships that help build and encourage us in our roles
3. Gender-specific retreats

CLEANSE THE MARRIAGE ROOM

We must clean the rooms of our hearts individually before we attempt to work through the issues at a relational level of reconciliation. Therefore, to clean our martial rooms we do not need our spouses to be involved at any level. Let's look at some of the steps we can use to access a redemptive flow into our marriages.

What Can I Do Now?

Evaluate your heart and everything that you have brought into the marriage that you recognize as unhealthy or impure. This may include defense mechanisms, control, shame, etc.

_____

_____

_____

Evaluate what your spouse has brought into the marriage that is unhealthy or impure.

_____

_____

_____

List the ways you have hurt or violated your spouse.

_____

_____

_____

List the ways your spouse has hurt or violated you.

_____

_____

_____

List how you have neglected to love or fulfill your role in your marriage.

_____

_____

_____

List how your spouse has neglected to love or fulfill his or her role in your marriage.

_____

_____

_____

Write your feelings regarding the pain and hurt you've carried in your relationship.

_____

_____

_____

Ask God to check your heart for any residue of resentments, bitterness, or anger towards your spouse.

_____

_____

_____

Action Steps

1. Call on God to dip your spouse into grace by bringing him or her into God's presence. Ask God to forgive the sins that he or she imposed on you, and to make his or her holiness the biggest priority of your marriage.

2. Call on God to cleanse your own heart by removing and forgiving the lists of failures, wrongdoings, and sins that occurred.

3. Pray for the cleanness of your own heart and the heart of your spouse. Ask God to make holiness the priority of your marriage, no matter the cost.

Write a letter to your spouse right now summarizing this process, including the hurts that have been revealed and the desire to offer and receive forgiveness from God.

_____

_____

_____

_____

_____

_____

_____

_____

_____

_____

_____

_____

_____

_____

_____

_____

_____

What Can We Do Together? Marriage Reconciliation

When a couple reconciles, the "built up" issues need to be cleansed first. This is necessary because those issues often caused deep levels of separation. But from there, forgiveness needs to be done on a daily basis. In fact, we can form a new habit of always forgiving our spouse and never allowing ourselves to go to sleep angry, resentful, or bitter. Forgiveness and grace is a lifestyle where we are constantly willing and ready to confess and repent—and also offer and receive forgiveness.

CLEANSING THE MARRIAGE FOR RECONCILIATION

Action Steps

1. Openly confess to each other the sins and shortcomings that you have committed, asking for forgiveness.
2. Pray for one another on a regular basis.
3. Cover the marriage with the blood of Jesus Christ—sealing and binding it from the separation that contaminated it in the past.
4. Speak God's truth over the marriage and each individual spouse's role and responsibility (the Enemy will attack by implanting lies and getting us to focus on our spouses' negative traits).
5. Take active steps towards making changes that indicate a true repentance has occurred.

GRIEVE

Some of the dreams and hopes we have in our marriages can be restored, and others may not. We will learn that God is redemptive despite what the people in our lives do. God gives us the gift of grief to effectively deal with emotions that emerge through this process. We must constantly remind ourselves to feel with the Lord—not medicate or run from our emotions.

What Can I Do Now?

Continue to add anything that you feel needs to be grieved into your "throne room." Grief will continue throughout your lifetime, so learning this exercise is to form a lifelong habit (see Chapter 2).

What Can We Do Together?

If we are seeking reconciliation through these principles, grief is something that can be done individually first, but can also be done together. Grief will always accompany repentance. When God draws us back to Himself and each other, there will always be a joy that also feels grief at the reality of sin. Through this experience together, we can learn to embrace grace at deeper levels towards ourselves and each other, recognizing that apart from God we are incapable and unable to live this life.

INTERCESSION

Marriage between and for the couple is the bedrock of everything it will produce. As we learned in Chapter 10, intercession prayer is powerful and must take on the purposes of God for our spouse's holiness above anything else.

What Can I Do Now?

If your marriage is difficult and contains separation, pray over your spouse and your marriage everyday—but call on God's plans, holiness, and purpose as the main objectives. These three areas are effective tools:

A House that Grace Built Workbook

1. Be consistent in prayer over your spouse every day.
2. Pray for the righteousness and spiritual needs of your spouse first and foremost before resolving only the external circumstances.
3. Ask God to give you a compassionate heart towards your spouse, separating who that person is from what he/she does.

What Can We Do Together?

If your marriage is operating in togetherness, pray with your spouse everyday—call on God to bring the marriage into the completion of His plans, His purposes, and His foundation of holiness. These two areas are especially effective:

1. Commit to a specific time every day to pray together, being consistent.
2. Bring specific situations and needs to the relationship openly before the Lord so you can share in the answers and grow together in the work that God performs through prayer.

THE ROOM OF DIVORCE

If you've been through a divorce, please take some time to revisit that relationship by entering and cleansing that room. It is important to assure that there isn't residue left within that marriage that may continue to affect you.

TRUTH TELLING EXERCISE

What do you feel most about the marriage in your life that ended in divorce? Do you feel anger, regret, sadness, etc.?

_____

_____

_____

What was your greatest failure in that relationship?

_____

_____

_____

What was your ex-spouse's violation/failure towards you?

_____

_____

_____

- 88 -

How did you deal with problems while in that marriage?

_____

_____

_____

How are you dealing with the reality of the divorce right now?

_____

_____

_____

Action Steps
1. If you are ready to forgive, simply bring that person into the Holy of Holies and present them before God. Ask God to wash away the sins that were committed against you, being willing to forgive and release.
2. In the same manner, ask God to place His blood on you to deal with all the things that broke down on your side. Receive God's forgiveness, recognizing that He will release you from the past.
3. Release that person and yourself to Jesus.
4. Renounce any soul ties that were formed in the marriage, asking God to remove anything that continues to bind you to that person wrongfully. If the enemy found a doorway of access or permission, remove the legal right, and forbid him future access (once forgiveness occurs, there is no legal right). Command any spiritual influence other than the Holy Spirit be released as a result of that soul tie (we did this already in Chapter 4).
5. Grieve the losses that may have been felt.
6. Pray for that person.

THE ROOM OF DEATH

The death of a spouse is typically one of the most painful experiences we can have in this lifetime. The only way to deal with that loss is through a healthy form of grief. How long we grieve may vary. God desires to heal our hearts and preserve the sacred memories acquired. If there was something negative in the marriage, we need to make sure we effectively cleanse that room sometime in the future. We can use the same process already explained in this chapter. But what we don't want to do is bypass effective grief and recycle a relationship into our lives improperly. We also need to deal with despair, depression, or other extremely negative emotions that may result, committing to seek God's comfort. Some other ways to deal with the loss of a spouse:

* Find a support group or spiritual community where you can be surrounded by people who can encourage you and love you.
* Pray for God's purposes and plans for your life, knowing that He is aware of your situation and has already prepared a pathway for your life.
* Ask to gain an eternal perspective of the relationship (see Chapter 20).

CHAPTER 13
REDEEMING THE ROOMS OF CHILDREN
Based on Chapter 13 of *A House that Grace Built*

As parents, we desire the best for our children, hoping to raise them in a healthy way so they eventually thrive and grow. When our own relationships and emotional issues strain the parenting role, it can have a direct effect on how we parent. God doesn't want to point out our flaws to hurt and cause us despair, but to help us and intervene in our situations. God is our perfect Father, both to us personally and to our children. We can rely on the faithfulness of His power.

In this chapter, we looked at the different purposes and breakdowns of the parenting role. We were asked to confront how our own parenting style may have affected our children. While "owning" our part is important, we also learned that much of parenting in our grown children is about learning to release. Furthermore, we can't be responsible for the choices our children make as adults, despite our influence. Thus, we need to learn to parent from God's redemptive purposes.

Chapter Highlights
- Assessing parenting styles
- Redeeming the rooms of our children
- Developing healthy intimacy

Homework Purpose
Working through the projects in this chapter is vital in assuring that we effectively deal with any shame, guilt or other issues that may have caused contamination in our children's rooms. In fact, if we have shame influencing our role as a parent, it is likely to perpetuate an overall unhealthy cycle. By learning to claim God's authority and His grace, we can begin to respond in these relationships with God's tools of authentic love. Above all, we are asked to pray and trust God in all matters pertaining to our children.

ASSESSING OUR PARENTAL STYLES

The influence and impact we made upon our children cannot be denied. But that's not to say that our mistakes, deficiencies or failures are permanent, nor that God can't intervene. By seeing the areas in our parenting styles where damage may have taken place, we can better prepare for a healthy transition into this role in the future.

PARENTING AND MARRIAGE

Marriage is meant to be the foundation of parenting; therefore, its failure or strain can deeply affect the children involved.

Have you experienced parenthood with a failed or unstable marriage operating at the core?

_____

_____

_____

Can you recognize how that affected your children? What do you predominantly feel as a result?

_____

_____

_____

Have you allowed God to deal with that in your heart?

_____

_____

_____

IDENTIFY ATTACHMENT STYLES

How we learn to attach to our children can lie in direct correlation with how our parents attached to us.

Can you recognize any attachment styles with your children that may have broken down?

_____

_____

_____

How does that affect your relationship with your children right now?

_____

_____

_____

IDENTIFY OUR DISCIPLINE TECHNIQUES

Healthy discipline is at the foundation of parenting. If we had a misunderstanding of love and discipline, we can unknowingly bring a tainted form of discipline into our parenting role. Let's assess this in the more detail.

How does love and discipline work in your children's (not adult children) lives?

_____

_____

_____

If they are grown, how did it work when they were under your care? Can you identify any snare in your own style?

_____

_____

_____

CLEANSING THE ROOMS OF OUR CHILDREN

Whatever failures may have been revealed in this process, it's never too late for the God of the Universe to initiate restoration. The entire purpose of grace is to meet us in failure and help us where we are unable. It simply takes a willingness on our part to give God access into our children's rooms.

For each individual child, list the ways you feel you have failed in your role as a parent. Include any specific violations or sin issues (use separate paper if necessary for each child).

_____

_____

_____

Write what grieves your heart about the upbringing you provided each child.

_____

_____

_____

List the issues you have with each individual child and any resentment you may carry about their behavior, rebellion, etc. Include any ways you have failed to deal with this appropriately.

_____

_____

_____

Action step

Write a letter to each child and share your heart, your apology, your testimony, and your desire to love them. Only share this letter if God prompts your heart.

Applying Redemption

Perhaps there is nothing that hurts us more than acknowledging our mistakes could have hurt our children. At the same time, there is nothing God wants more than to teach us that He is sufficient to deal with their needs since He is already their perfect Heavenly Father.

Action Steps

1. Bring your lists into your throne room; confess and repent of any wrongdoing. Ask God to cover it and blot it out through His blood and forgiveness.
2. Bring each child into that throne room and declare the sufficiency of God's grace over every mistake or failure you have made, surrendering them to Him as their perfect Father.
3. If your children are still dependent by age, develop a plan of action for parenting. Incorporate other parental resources and tools once you have placed redemptive principles within each room (if you skip redemption, the other tools won't work because the overall system will be broken). We recommend *Next Level Parenting* by Rich Rogers and a variety of parental materials by James Dobson.
4. If your children are adults, but you have allowed them to maintain dependence on you, come up with a plan of action to help them attain independence apart from your direct care for them. This may have to happen gradually to ensure that they are equipped (if irresponsible or addictive behaviors are present, a more firm action plan will be required. Additional resources are needed for this. We recommend *The Christian Family Guide to Addiction and Recovery* by Robert and Stephanie Tucker

Intercession

Intercede for your child at every point and in every way. Make prayer the absolute priority of your job as a parent. If your children live with you, pray with them as much as they will allow, but pray for them continually as an act of entrusting their lives to God's care. If your children are grown, use prayer as your primary way of loving them, relying more on God's power and less on your own acts towards them.

The Room of Abortion

If we have experienced an abortion, it's important that we face and allow God to heal that room in our hearts. Depending on how denial played a factor in the decision, we may or may not have come in touch with the grief associated with an abortion.

This project will help us face and connect with the reality of abortion, and learn how God's grace can cover and heal this room in our hearts. (If at any point you find this process overwhelming or difficult, please seek the assistance of a counselor or pastor. Please see our "Resource Guide" in *A House that Grace Built*.

Facing Truth

How have you dealt with the abortion after it occurred?

_____

_____

_____

Have you connected to the reality that the baby was an actual human life, with unique features, DNA, and features that were derived from your own body or the body of your partner?

_____

_____

_____

Applying Redemption
Action Steps

1. Write a letter to God expressing your sadness for the abortion. Admit and confess your wrongdoing. Ask for forgiveness. After acknowledging your wrongdoing, stand before Him with open arms and commit this area of your heart to Him.
2. Ask God to remove the burden of shame and guilt, and cover you with His righteous blood.
3. Ask God to receive your baby until you are able to meet in person (He already has done this, but in our own hearts we need to be willing to release our children to Him).
4. When feelings of guilt and shame attack you, rather than view your sin and wrongdoing, view God holding and loving your baby, caring for him or her in your place. Rather than hold onto the pain of your own wrongdoing, look at the marvelous reality of grace. A true understanding

of this should drop you to the ground and make you humbly and deeply praise the awesome glory and love of a God who always is in charge, who reigns supremely, and who always offers us a method of redemption.

GRIEVE

With abortion, the entire process of healing will include admitting (confessing), seeking forgiveness and grieving. Grief is an extremely important aspect to dealing with abortion because it entails the ability to release the pain of the situation. If you have not yet connected enough with the situation emotionally to grieve, continue to pray and ask God to allow you to feel over the baby. To assist you with this, you can:

1. Write the baby a letter and apologize for not giving him or her a chance at life. This may be deeply painful if you have not yet grieved; therefore, get the support you need if you feel unable to do this alone.
2. Name the baby as a way of honoring his or her life and affirming the child's value and preciousness.
3. Attend an abortion support group, such as "White as Snow" ministries.

THE DEATH OF A CHILD

Dealing with the loss of a child requires an individual healing process that takes time and the supernatural resources of God's love and grace. No parents could ever "get over" the physical departure of a child, yet should be able to experience peace and release over a period of time as healing occurs. That's because death on this side of this world leads to that child's eternal prosperity. Yet that does not minimize the pain of the separation that has occurred and the dreams that were perhaps broken or lost.

All death needs to be dealt with through a form of grieving. We must remember that authentic grief gets hindered when the wound is not clean. This can happen when:

- We carry deep levels of shame and guilt over the relationship, thus cannot forgive ourselves or allow God to forgive us
- Carry deep resentments towards someone else responsible for the loss
- Continue to stay in denial in order to not have to feel the pain
- Find alternative ways to "check out" from having to cope with the death (such as drugs or alcohol)

If you have lost a child, it is something that only you and the Lord can work through together. Please seek the help of a pastor or Christian counselor to assist in this, and find others who have journeyed through the same crisis. Gaining an eternal perspective (Chapter 20) is truly the hope and anchor we can carry throughout the rest of our lifetime on earth. The hope we have as Christians is in the eternal, not the immediate circumstances.

CHAPTER 14
UNTANGLING OUR OUTER COURTS
Based on Chapter 14 of *A House that Grace Built*

The outer courts in codependence had distorted purposes. We often used them to cover the underlining sense of pain, insecurity, loneliness, fear, and shame. While our outward "homes" may have "looked good," our inward realities were in desperate need of God's intervention. In fact, in codependence we had often reversed the purpose of the outer courts, using them to wrongfully attempt to fill our inner-most need for acceptance and love. While facing and admitting this may have been difficult, by continuing through the process of healing, we discover that God releases us from this mentality, and He begins to implement a lifestyle of authenticity. Thus, the outer courts will begin to be aligned with God-given purpose.

Chapter Highlights
- Assessing friendships
- Assessing our role in ministry
- Untangling the courts

Homework Purpose

In Chapter 14 we evaluated some key areas of our outer courts and assessed any wrongful mentalities we may have brought into that area. This evaluation process prepared us to cleanse the outer courts, and be alert when it reverts to being used outside of its intended purposes. As we will continue to learn, our outer courts is a reflection of the status of our Holy of Holies and inner court; thus, when problems arise, we will need to continue to trace the deeper roots.

ASSESSING OUR OUTER COURTS

As we see the distortions and issues presented in our inner courts, we can better comprehend how the outer courts of lives were used improperly. In fact, often our outer court was being used to fill or medicate the inner hurts we harbored. Assessing the exact nature of how we functioned in our outer courts is helpful.

ASSESSING FRIENDSHIPS

As we learned in Chapter 8, friendships are an important part of lives, but need to be established within their proper context. Oftentimes our styles and patterns of friendship become contaminated through the filter of our codependence. Therefore, it's important that we learn to assess each one and recognize our role and responsibility in it.

Do you see patterns where you have established friendships where you overly give or put yourself in an authority role? How does that affect the relationship?

_____

_____

_____

Do you see patterns where you want to be on the receiving end of a relationship, and you place high demands as a result? How does that affect the relationship?

_____

_____

_____

Do you see that you fear authority or try to dismantle it in subtle ways? Explain. How does this trace to your own experience with authority systems?

_____

_____

_____

CLEANSING OUR FRIENDSHIPS

God will begin to teach us how to distinguish healthy friendships from unhealthy friendships. As we become aware of this, it's not that God asks that we begin to "kick" people out; rather, He wants to teach us to not engage and interact through an unhealthy relational style. Let's take a look.

What friendships contain unhealthy soul ties? Refer to your lists in Chapter 4 or refresh your list as needed.

_____

_____

_____

What has motivated you to remain in friendships that were not healthy? What did you fear in losing that friendship?

_____

_____

_____

List your close friends. Are they able to be mutually giving in a relationship with you?

_____

_____

_____

Are there any people listed that should have an outreach purpose instead?

_____

_____

_____

Are there any listed that do not have fellowship in the Spirit?

_____

_____

_____

Action Steps
Bring your outer court and inner court friendships into the "Holy of Holies" and ask God to purify them, cleanse them, and release them into His purpose.

1. Deal with any specific relationships that need to undergo the process of forgiveness. This includes relationship where you have been harmed, or you have harmed someone.
2. Pray for your friendships.

ASSESSING THE OUTER COURTS OF THE BODY OF CHRIST
How we engaged in ministry as a member of the body of Christ was often tainted by our codependence. We unknowingly used the church environment improperly to deal with the missing or invalidated needs in our personal lives. This next section will help reveal our own areas of weakness, as well as help us to understand the central purpose of service to God.

Describe how you function in your public role within the body of Christ?

_____

_____

_____

Is there anything you know to be pretentious? And if so, why do you feel that you can't be real?

_____

_____

_____

List the current ministry work you do, and begin to pray over it and ask for God's priority. Is there anything that immediately needs to change? Write it down.

_____

_____

_____

Do you use church ministry as a priority over your own family needs? Why do you think this is?

_____

_____

_____

PLACING REDEMPTION IN OUR MINISTRY WORK

God wouldn't ask that we give up ministry altogether. He is building His church and has equipped us to participate! Rather, He will ask that our ministry work be purified and empowered through His giftedness, not our codependence. Therefore, we want to ask Him to lead and direct us in this area of our lives. Releasing our ministry means God can redirect us, or can even detach us for a season. But it will most assuredly lead us into our God-given calling and purpose.

Action Steps
1. Make intimacy with God your primary ministry and mission by coming to Him, spending time with Him, and seeking His love before doing anything else.
2. Ask God to cleanse and purify your heart in this area, redeeming His plans and purposes.
3. Pray for specific direction in each ministry God has called to you, being willing to release that which is not of Him.
4. Write each ministry in your "throne room" under the "release" section of the journal.

ASSESSING ACTIVITY

How we spend our time and assign worth to activity is an important aspect of long-term recovery. In codependence we often focused on the priorities of other people, to the neglect of our own needs or responsibilities. Continually asking God to purify and clear our schedules from unwanted or unneeded activity is helpful.

Action Steps

1. Write a weekly schedule of activity to organize your week.
2. Begin to pray over each activity it contains.
3. As you go about your day, ask God to reveal if you are functioning through His resources first, or if you are seeking to be filled by something you are doing.
4. Be willing to make adjustments as God brings clarity and life circumstances change.

ASSESSING OUR "THINGS"

One of God's functions in our lives is that of a provider. When we are in a relationship with Him, the things He provides will align with His purpose and His will. But when we see things apart from Him, we can either overly assert value to materialistic things, or we can fear that our needs will not be met. Let's spend time assessing our own relationship to "things."

List the things or needs that cause your heart anxiety.

_____

_____

_____

What do you fear the most about not having enough material needs or losing what you have?

_____

_____

_____

Action Steps

1. Pray over the material necessities and claim God's provision for them
2. When anxiety and fear consume you, cling to God's promise and speak them back to God. Believe that God is Your provider
3. Assess your attachment to "things" on a daily basis, asking God to be willing to release anything you have.

UNTANGLING OUR COURTS

In redeeming the rooms of our heart, we will find specific things that needed to be dealt with, but we will oftentimes come in touch with overall patterns. Identify your own patterns in your outer courts.

Explain what your outer courts looked like before you entered into recovery. Describe the specific activities and what motivated you.

_____

_____

_____

What do your outer courts look like today? What is the biggest change?

_____

_____

_____

Where are you most vulnerable to being motivated by external people, activity, things and circumstances?

_____

_____

_____

CHAPTER 15
FORTIFYING OUR HEARTS
Based on Chapter 15 of *A House that Grace Built*

While we seek to remove unhealthy defense strategies and secure our lives with healthy protection, the first task is to seek God and utilize His resources rather than our self-efforts. This begins by allowing God to conquer our hearts within, claim ownership over us, and thus be willing to walk under His covering and provision for us.

As we learned, the threat in our lives oftentimes isn't the outside influences as much as what we claim to be the truth in our lives. Whenever we believe or allow something into our lives that is not of God, we become extremely vulnerable to being harmed.

We learned that in order to be victorious, God did not leave us powerless and defenseless. Instead, He gave us weapons and tools to fight the Enemy's strategies. The weapons directly refer to the tools we have gained thus far in recovery, therefore, they are extremely relevant to what we have acquired thus far.

Chapter Highlights
- Assessing the threat
- Walking protected
- Understanding our weapons

Homework Purpose
Theology is much different than our actual experience. Even though we have understood these familiar weapons from our previous studies, the purpose of this application project is to see how these are in operation in our own lives. By learning how to link these weapons with the tools of our recovery, we'll discover that God has already equipped us and continues to strengthen us to defend ourselves through Him.

ASSESSING THE THREAT

We oftentimes fight the relational battles in our lives as though they are entirely "human" problems. Yet the Word of God is clear that our battles have a spiritual origin, and we do not actually fight against "flesh and blood." While this is an uncomfortable and sometimes inconvenient truth, we must become aware of the divisive nature of the Enemy in human relationships so we can become better armed to defend, protect, and love as God intended in those situations.

Can you identify how the enemy tries to plant divisive lies into your close relationships?

_____

_____

_____

Have you dealt with them as a human problem? Can you recognize that there is a larger scheme to ruin that relationship?

_____

_____

_____

Action Step

In this next week, pay special attention to the situations you face. See if you can trace the belief systems that are driving you to see a person negatively in your life (if applicable). In Chapter 17 we will look at ways to specifically deal with these conflicts.

UNDERSTANDING OUR WEAPONS OF WARFARE

Most of us have been exposed to the biblical picture of spiritual warfare. We may be quite familiar with the passage on spiritual weapons and even have presumed to understand it. Yet learning how to make those weapons a practical reality in our lives is altogether different. In this next section, we want to look at the spiritual weapons listed in God's Word and apply them to the recovery process. Please refer to the principles contained in Chapter 15 that highlight and detail each weapon, and then answer the following questions.

BELT OF TRUTH

Explain how truth has set you free and what you can continue to do to assure victory.

_____

_____

_____

How do you use discernment to protect yourself?

_____

_____

_____

Do you see any breaches in the armor of truth in your own life? How does the enemy attack you most in this area?

_____

_____

_____

ARMOR OF RIGHTEOUSNESS

How do you assert your sense of righteousness?

_____

_____

_____

If the enemy attacks you in this area, what will it look like?

_____

_____

_____

What have you depended on in the past to gain your sense of righteousness?

_____

_____

_____

SHOES OF PEACE

Describe the relationships in your life that are spiritually imbalanced. How do you handle them?

_____

_____

_____

Instead of using words, what activity can you bring to those relationships?

_____

_____

_____

What is the most important ingredient in sharing your testimony and Jesus with those around you?

_____

_____

_____

SHIELD OF FAITH

Describe the operation of faith in your own life. Where do you fail to believe in God?

_____

_____

_____

Is there a situation right now where you've given up hope in God's promises?

_____

_____

_____

Explain how the Enemy tried to defeat you in your confidence and identity in Jesus Christ.

_____

_____

_____

What will your response be the next time you recognize such an attack?

_____

_____

_____

SWORD OF THE SPIRIT

Explain how the sword can be used to pierce an attack.

_____

_____

_____

Can you recognize where you are most vulnerable to believing Satan's lies?

_____

_____

_____

How can you prepare to take the sword against those lies?

_____

_____

_____

PRAYER

Describe the use of prayer in your life. Do you see it as a duty, activity, or obligation? Or do you see it as a continuous form of "talking" with God?

_____

_____

_____

Why is prayer so effective in fighting a spiritual war?

_____

_____

CHAPTER 16
AFFIRMING THE GATES OF GLORY

Based on Chapter 16 of A House that Grace Built

We often don't think of God as having boundaries. Yet His entire operation in His relationship towards us occurs by clearly distinguishing His role from ours. In essence, He stakes out who He is and what He will allow in relationship with us. He tells us where we belong in Him, what He enables and desires us to do, and where He must claim His rightful position as the Sovereign God of the Universe. Since God doesn't sin, His boundaries are always pure, and He cannot go against His character. On the other hand, since we possess a sin nature, we will constantly be breaking the boundaries He establishes. That's why God's role above anything always has redemptive power.

Sometimes our misunderstanding of God caused us to place boundaries in our hearts that kept God out. Other times, we took on roles that were meant to be fulfilled only by God. Through this recovery process, we learn how to stand and exist in relationship with God based on His character and grace towards us. We learn to trust and love Him. We learn that we can walk in our part, through His power, and we can cease trying to do things we don't have the ability to do. The more we learn to rely on God's resources, the more faithful He can prove Himself to us.

Chapter Highlights

- What God gives us
- What God does not share
- What we give God

Homework Purpose

In this chapter we sought to understand the basic activity of our Holy of Holies. We looked at what we do to receive from God, how we give back to Him and where we place our overall trust in moment by moment life decisions.

We also assessed our vulnerabilities in our relationship with God, finding where our weaknesses caused His role or our own roles to be skewed.

BASIC NEEDS

Throughout life we will carry some basic needs that we will by default seek to satisfy. By learning to depending on God, we will find a secure foundation of having these needs met. That's because He does not change and is always faithful to His promises. Our vulnerability will be to look to satisfy our basic needs outside our relationship with God. Let's take a closer look.

Basic need: a deep desire for love. Where do you go when you want to be loved?

_____

_____

_____

Basic need: a longing for acceptance. How do you deal with your need for acceptance?

_____

_____

_____

Basic need: a sense of security and safety. What makes you feel safe and secure?

_____

_____

_____

Basic need: purpose and usefulness. What makes you feel valuable and needed?

_____

_____

_____

WHAT GOD GIVES US

Learning to live and walk by God's Spirit means we first need to accept what He offers to us. If at any point we turn away from the Source and seek to meet our needs independently of God, we'll be led back into different forms of bondage. Let's assess how we operate in the three areas that were covered in Chapter 16.

His Resources

Can you picture yourself entering into the spiritual warehouse of the Holy of Holies and grabbing the "supplies" you need to live this life? How do you actually access those?

_____

_____

_____

His Cleansing

Can you picture coming to God with an expectant and confident hope that He gladly is ready to receive and cleanse you on a daily basis, delighting in making you beautiful and whole? If not, what makes that scenario difficult?

_____

_____

_____

His Wisdom

Can you picture God as the "control room" of your life, offering you the guidance and direction you need to know where to go and how to arrive at the next destination He has purposed for you? When you feel a lack of direction, how do you handle it?

_____

_____

_____

WHAT GOD WILL NOT SHARE WITH US

There are aspects of God's character that cannot be shared or accessed by us. They are reserved for God and are reasons to give Him praise and glory far above human beings.

Can you identify any area where you knowingly or unknowingly attempted to receive something that did not belong to anyone but God? Describe.

_____

_____

_____

Can you identify any area where you knowingly or unknowingly attempted to give a person something that only belonged to God? Describe.

_____

_____

_____

WHAT WE GIVE TO GOD

As we learn to give God His rightful position and receive His love and resources on a continual basis, it will prompt a desire to give back to Him. When we live in the delightful reality of what grace has done for us, we will want to give gifts back to God in loving response.

Can you identify where you honestly are able to give back to God based on His love towards you?

_____

_____

_____

Can you identify where you honestly are not giving to God what is due to Him? Because this is never a behavioral issue, try to identify the spiritual belief behind it, if possible.

_____

_____

_____

Action Steps
1. Take the core issues that have been revealed in this chapter and write them in your journal under "release."
2. Pray that God would teach you to live by Him, rely on Him, and in turn give back to Him through affection, love, and obedience.

CHAPTER 17
SECURING OUR INNER COURTS

Based on Chapter 17 of *A House that Grace Built*

As we learn how to exist in relationship with God, we become equipped to better understand the purpose and valid "gates" in human relationships. Yet in dealing with our human relationships, it will always prove to be difficult because we not only have to address our own issues, but we deal with all the problems another human being brings into the relationship.

Therefore, as we learn to secure what God purified in our hearts and lives, we need to develop a healthy gate system where we learn to respect others and ask that they respect us. We also need to learn to deal with the deficiencies and problems that arise in our relationships. This is an enormous task that cannot be fulfilled by merely staking out "to do" lists. It must come by first engaging in relationship with a loving and powerful God—being able to take on His heart and mind, and carry the weapons He has given us to use on a daily basis.

Chapter Highlights

- Gate of respect
- Gate of expectations
- Conflict resolution

Homework Purpose

In this chapter we looked at a variety of difficulties that can arise in our human relationships within our inner courts, and addressed some of the key ways God calls us to respond biblically. We also sought to understand the ingredients of a healthy gate system, and how to deal with the threats that arise on a continual basis with those whom we are closely connected. This chapter offered a variety of tools to help sift, soft and properly understand the nature of each relational challenge we may face now or in the future.

THE GATE OF RESPECT

Gates are designed to respect the boundary of someone else's property. When we lack respect, we ignore, discount, or invalidate it in the process. This not only shows disregard for the gate itself, but for everything that was meant to be protected or reserved for privacy behind it. In codependence, our gates of respect were extremely broken and run down in a variety of ways. People trampled our gates and entered into areas meant to be protected. Oftentimes we participated by removing our gates altogether and allowing people inside. Over time, we didn't even have gates.

When we lack an understanding of the gate of respect, we usually disrespect other people's gates as a result. Thus, we ourselves often "jump" gates and disrespect people by making choices on their behalf. Let's take a closer look at how some of the gates of respect can be breached.

RESPECT AND SUBMISSION

While we are asked to respect ourselves and each other, we also need to know where God calls us to submit and "give up" rights in certain situations. This is a very delicate area in our lives and requires some thoughtful consideration.

In a given situation, when we are asked to do something for someone or submit to another person's will or ideas, we need to run it through a filter (see next page). In essence, we need to understand God's perspective, His calling to us and the exact nature of what is occurring in that situation. We don't want to submit wrongfully, but just the same, we are obligated to submit through God's principles.

Action Steps
1. Identify relationship challenges that require submission based on respect.
2. Run that situation through the "filter of respect worksheet" on the next page.
3. Pray for God to teach and reveal His will so submission and respect become a natural response in given situation.

RESPECT AND FREEDOM

Whenever we gave up our abilities to think, feel, and act for ourselves, we essentially were controlled by other people and influences in their lives. Similarly, when we sought control in relationships, we attempted to manipulate a person's thoughts, feelings, or decisions.

In this chapter we looked at the gates of freedom from several different perspectives to understand where our own intrusions occurred. Let's take a look.

THE GATES OF OUR BODY

Have you been placed in a situation where your physical body was not respected; thus, it caused a tainted understanding of your preciousness and worth?

_____

_____

_____

THE FILTER OF RESPECT WORKSHEET

Would doing this violate a specific truth in the Word of God?
_____ Yes _____ No Explain.

_____

_____

_____

Would doing this ask me to disrespect the truth of who I am in the Word of God?
_____ Yes _____ No Explain.

_____

_____

_____

Would doing this cause me to compromise or put someone or something above God?
_____ Yes _____ No Explain.

_____

_____

_____

What makes me not want to submit (personal desire, need, preference, emotions, etc.)?

_____

_____

_____

What will happen if I submit? What will happen if I don't submit?

_____

_____

_____

What would God want me to do?

_____

_____

_____

Have you violated someone in this area?

_____

_____

_____

Action Steps

1. Confess and repent of your responsibility.
2. Pray and forgive those who have violated you.
3. Pray over any activity that occurred that caused a breach in the gate of your physical life. Whether it was willful or not, pray to claim ownership and rights to your physical body.

THE GATES OF OUR THOUGHTS

Do you see where you allowed someone else to think for you? (This is also the unhealthy soul tie that was revealed in Chapter 4.)

_____

_____

_____

Do you attempt to control how someone else thinks in a given situation?

_____

_____

_____

Action Steps

1. Confess and repent of your responsibility.
2. Pray and forgive those who have violated you.
3. In all situations, begin to claim the truth of God and reject the lies.

THE GATES OF OUR EMOTIONS

Do you hold something or someone else responsible for how you feel?

_____

_____

_____

Do you think you can change how someone else feels?

_____

_____

_____

Action Steps
1. Confess and repent of your responsibility.
2. Pray and forgive those who have violated you.
3. Believe that all truths about God can overcome toxic emotions by stabilizing us and providing us with peace, joy, and comfort—even in the midst of difficulties.
4. Pray over your emotional needs and issues that arise. In the heat of the battle, ask God to reveal a stabilizing truth that can help you to connect to Him above and beyond the emotional struggles you face.

THE GATES OF PURPOSE AND IDENTITY
Have you believed the identity someone else imposed on you?

_____

_____

_____

Have you tried to make someone into the image or idea of what you wanted them to be?

_____

_____

_____

Action Steps
1. Confess and repent of your responsibility.
2. Pray and forgive those who have violated you.
3. Assert your identity in Christ on a daily and minute-to-minute basis.

THE GATES OF MARRIAGE AND FAMILY ROLES
Do you see how your role was disrespected by a parent or spouse?

_____

_____

_____

Do you see how you disrespected the role of a parent of spouse?

_____

_____

_____

Do you see how your role as a child was disrespected in your upbringing?

_____

_____

_____

Do you see how you may have disrespected your own children?

_____

_____

_____

Action Steps
1. Confess and repent your responsibility.
2. Pray and forgive those who have violated you. (You should have already gone through this process in previous chapters.)
3. Honor the God-given roles as He designed them to be, and pray for God to give you the ability to fulfill your role and encourage your family members in their roles.

THE GATE OF EXPECTATIONS

Expectations play a significant role in how we relate to people. We typically bring to a relationship a set of expectations of what we want people to do for us. We also bring criteria of what we want from them. Much of the time, our expectations are unrealistic and attached to unmet needs in our lives prior to entering into a relationship. We may be operating from ideals rather than the reality of how people can actually love us.

Forming healthy expectations doesn't mean we need to allow bad behavior; rather, we need to come to accept and meet people where they are, expecting them to provide what they are able to give. We must also assign gates to our own hearts, and keep people who are a threat to us at a safe distance.

Learning to set healthy expectations is no easy task and will require time with the Lord to understand how He deals with us in this area. In truth, God expects nothing from us other than what He's first given to us. We must learn to use this same expectation in our relationships with each other.

Evaluating Our Expectations

What expectations do you carry in your inner court relationships? Take time to list them in the following relationships:

Parents

_____

_____

_____

Spouse

_____

_____

_____

Children

_____

_____

_____

Close Friends

_____

_____

_____

What expectations do you believe they carry towards you in that same relationship?

Parents

_____

_____

_____

Spouse

_____

_____

_____

Children

_____

_____

_____

Close Friends

_____

_____

_____

Do you see any unrealistic expectations? Write them each down.

_____

_____

_____

EXPECTATIONS IN SPIRITUALLY IMBALANCED SITUATIONS

When we are dealing with someone who isn't able to connect and receive God's resources in the relationship, that relationship becomes instantly imbalanced. That person cannot offer what they have not yet received. This is a difficult situation, because their inability to love us properly can hurt us tremendously. To help us work through relationships with this scenario, we are going to work through a project reserved for our close relationships.

Action Steps
1. List your current difficult relationships with people who are not spiritually discerned.
2. If these are common and daily relationships, take some time to write the dialogue that takes place with this person. Track conversations as much as you can for one week (see "Tracking Difficult Relationships Worksheet" on the next page).
3. Pray over the discussions and the issues that are brought up in the relationship. Ask the Lord to help you understand and discern the spiritual nature of that situation.

APPLYING BOUNDARIES
(For a full definition of boundaries, refer to TCCRW: From Surviving to Significance, Chapter 11).

Learning how to see the breakdowns occurring in our relationship is important. But learning how to respond appropriately entails the true growth of our recovery (we will discuss this in a later section). We must understand we won't do this perfectly. However, by learning a basic formula in applying boundaries we can begin to equip ourselves effectively. This includes:

- Understanding our authority in Christ (His truth, our rights, our responsibilities and godly protection)
- Understanding the authority of the earthly role (We cannot unsurp God-given authority roles)
- Respecting God's point of view in our lives
- Respecting God's point of view of other people in our lives
- Protecting our holiness
- Making holiness of the other person a priority

TRACKING DIFFICULT RELATIONSHIPS WORKSHEET
Track relationship dialogue and write down pieces of conversation that reflect both sides.
Use separate paper if necessary

WHAT HE/SHE SAYS   WHAT I SAY

In Chapter 17 we looked at an example of learning how to apply boundaries effectively. We learned that when dealing with someone who isn't spiritually discerned, our expectations are limited. We simply can't ask them to change their behaviors or attitudes. What we can do is determine an appropriate "healthy gate" in the situation. This means we can set a gate that will determine how much of their influence we'll allow to affect our lives. In order to do this, we must always be willing to first own our responsibility in the situation.

Physical boundary

If our safety, health or sometimes our emotional or spiritual well-being is being jeopardized, we may need to physically separate from a person. This does not need to apply to all situations, thus we need wisdom and insight before taking action.

A physical boundary means we take action at an external level. The goal of such a boundary is to protect our hearts, and allow that person the opportunity to get help. This separation doesn't need to be permanent. It might only be a few minutes, hours, days, or even months.

Time and consideration can be given to the restoration of the relationship if the violator receives help and restoration. God may lead us out of that situation permanently, but initially the separation may be necessary to gain proper perspective. Any form of physical abuse is included in this category. If you are in an abusive situation, you must seek help to assist in this process.

Separation is not the only physical boundary. We may have other forms of consequences that may be necessary based on our role in the relationship. Remember, we can't imposed child-like discipline onto adult relationships, or give adult-like consequences to our young children. We must apply consequences in direct correlation to their established authority system.

Emotional boundary

An emotional boundary is not tangible, but exists inside our own heart. Therefore, when we set an emotional boundary, we are protecting the intrusion of a belief system to affect our emotions negatively. For example, if someone is saying hurtful words that attempt to sabotage our sense of worth, the emotional boundary is that we first reject those words, and choose to focus on God's truth. It doesn't mean it won't hurt. We will need to learn to effectively cope with that pain with the Lord. We can establish an emotional boundary without telling the other person to change. We do this by receiving God's love and truth in the situation. However, there are occasions where a physical boundary may eventually be necessary.

Spiritual boundary

A spiritual boundary describes our commitment to God based on what He permits or does not permit in our lives. We've spent significant time learning about this. At a foundational level, a spiritual boundary means we will not compromise or allow someone else's opinion or ideas to supercede God's truth. We cannot impose God onto people or force them to believe our point of view. Rather, we can reject any attempt to dismantle God's truth. In other words, we can't change people, but we won't allow them to influence our belief system either. Learning this boundary is difficult because God is invested in their redemption, not merely protecting us against their behavior. He calls us to love our enemies because that is the most powerful way of displaying and honoring God's character to someone who doesn't know Him. Therefore, if we are legalistic and rude towards people who are spiritually ignorant, we do a great disservice to how God can reach that person. At the same time, we don't have to compromise. Not ever.

ASSIGNING BOUNDARIES IN IMBALANCED RELATIONSHIP

Refer to the chart on page 124. Use this formula to begin to develop a series of healthy gates (boundaries) in your own life. In order to be effective, you must continually:

1. Take note of your weaknesses and areas of vulnerability. Continue to constantly assess where your "triggers" cause you to go into codependent behaviors or react wrongfully.
2. With the Lord, develop some boundaries of how you can respond, how you must let go, and what you need to do in a given situation.
3. Write down your spiritual and earthly authority in that situation.
4. Pray for wisdom and direction.

EXPECTATIONS IN FUNCTIONAL FAMILIES

We can hold our family members accountable and openly address issues and conflict when we have a godly framework in which to work. This doesn't mean we can impose our ideas or expectations onto them, rather it means we can be mindful of God's plans or direction in that situation since we are mutually related to Him. We can also leave room for grace, and constantly implement forgiveness to deal with the problems and violations as they occur. If we are learning how to be healthy after having had alot of dysfunctional dynamics, we can incorporate the same tool as we learned in the past section. But before we do that, let's take a closer look our healthy inner court relationships.

Describe your close relationships where you and that person both house God's resources. If you have none, you do not need to complete this project, but stay focused on that relationship from God's perspective and His redemption plans.

_____

_____

_____

When issues arise in the relationship, how are they dealt with? Is communication allowed? Are feelings expressed? Is Jesus brought into the situation?

_____

_____

_____

If not, why do you think that is?

_____

_____

ASSIGNING BOUNDARIES IN UNHEALTHY RELATIONSHIPS WORKSHEET

Identifying Relationship Issues

Name the relationship:_____

What is my earthly authority role in this situation?

_____
_____
_____
_____
_____
_____

What is my spiritual authority? How does God permit me to use my spiritual authority in this situation?

_____
_____
_____
_____
_____
_____

How can I affirm self-respect towards God's principles in this situation? Am I focused on healthy protection or trying to change the outcome?

_____
_____
_____
_____
_____
_____

How can I affirm respect towards that person using God's principles in this situation?

_____
_____
_____
_____
_____
_____

Setting Healthy Gates
(Use separate paper if necessary)

Physical boundary. Where/when/what circumstances require that I physically separate from this person? What consequences will I impose if this boundary is breached? Are there other external consequences that may need to be imposed (financially, materially, etc.?)

_____
_____
_____
_____
_____

Emotional Boundary. How can I cope with negative situations that lead to my emotional reactions? How can I disallow negative emotions to penetrate? What will I do if I continue to be disrespected emotionally? Do I have a right to take external action, or is this a reality of the "fellowship of the sufferings of Christ that I must solely grieve with Him?

_____
_____
_____
_____

Spiritual boundary. I cannot submit to something that contradicts God's truth. If I'm asked to do this, how will I establish this boundary and what will the consequences be if it is disrespected?

_____
_____
_____
_____
_____

DEALING WITH CONFLICT

How we deal with conflict will determine the result. It's often not the problem itself that challenges and strains our relationship, but how we react in a given situation. Learning how to properly assess and deal with conflict is extremely important. Page 126 offers us a worksheet of how we can begin this process.

BIBLICAL CONFRONTATION

In dealing with conflicts biblically, we must first understand if we are dealing with a fellow brother or sister in Christ, or if we are dealing with someone who is not spiritually discerned. Sometimes, even Christians in our lives may be in such deep denial and strongholds, they are not able to understand or embrace truth. Thus, before we attempt to deal with the conflict, we must set the proper expectation for them. If they have nothing spiritual to bring to the relationship, then biblical confrontation is not possible. We are to instead treat that person as someone in need of a spiritual remedy.

However, if this person is a follower of Jesus Christ, we can follow biblical guidelines.

1. We are to confront that person privately about the issue that concerns us. Page 292 of *A House that Grace Built* listed some of the ways we can do this.
2. We can bring witnesses with us who can offer wise discernment. We should only do this when there is a need or a crisis that isn't being resolved in our own family system. This should not be used to get a pastor or counselor to "side" with our point of view.
3. The goal in every conflict is for confession and repentance to occur where there had been wrongdoing. Once this happens on either side of the relationship, the matter should be closed.

ADDRESSING CONFLICT WORKSHEET

What is my part? List all the ways you could be contributing to the problem. If you honestly don't think you are, you do not need to own responsibility.

_____

_____

_____

_____

What is the other's person's part? List all the ways they are contributing to the problem as you see it right now.

_____

_____

_____

_____

What does God's truth say in this situation? If God could audibly speak to you on this matter, what would He say? Remember, God operates by the truths stated in His Word. He cannot contradict Himself.

_____

_____

_____

How might the enemy be operating in this situation? The true strategy is to dismantle anything that the enemy is trying to use to cause division. Remember, people are never our enemies.

_____

_____

_____

Have you ever avoided confrontation and instead discussed the problem with other people? What was the result? Did that help or worsen the problem?

_____

_____

_____

CHAPTER 18
RESTORING OUR OUTER GATES

Based on Chapter 18 of *A House that Grace Built*

When our inner lives were broken, our outward gates could hardly protect us or provide us with security. As we learned in previous chapters, our outer courts were also very vulnerable to the allowances of unhealthy and dysfunctional relationships and situations.

By cleansing and purifying our inner courts, we became ready to utilize our outer courts properly. This means our outer courts can protect us, while at the same time house God-ordained activities. Thus our outer courts is a place where we can radiate and share God's love, without allowing unwanted intrusions to overtake our heart again.

Chapter 18 also helped us to understand how God leads and directs us in our decisions and lifestyle choices. As we learn how to submit to God in all situations, we will find that living under God's authority is a place of true freedom - where our desires will align with Him. A place where we won't focus on "what we do," but can stand firmly in the knowledge and protection of our identity in Christ.

Chapter Highlights
- Broken and repaired gates
- Strength and balance
- Knowing God's will

Homework Purpose

Chapter 18 allowed us to assess our outer courts, understanding how our gate system had operated in the past. We also looked at ways to learn how to function and be lead by God's purposes, allowing things into our lives that were first surrendered and approved by God. This lifestyle not only prepares us to live a fruitful and abundant life, it also prevents us from severely falling into the lifestyle of self-sufficiency.

Broken and Repaired Gates

Through recovery, we've learned to see and understand the areas of vulnerability we had in our outer gate system. This exposure, along with the healing that has transpired, gives us the ability to implement gates that have useful purposes.

Which gates can you identify that were areas of brokenness in your outer courts?

_____

_____

_____

How has recovery up to this point changed how you interact in your outer courts?

_____

_____

_____

What is your biggest area of vulnerability?

_____

_____

_____

Action Steps
1. Continually pray over vulnerabilities and ask God to cover you by His grace.
2. Ask God to continually show you how to allow people into your life in a healthy way, recognizing that this takes work and time to establish.

Balance & Strength

Learning how to balance and stay spiritually strong in the activity and relationships in our outer courts will occur as we mature in the Lord. The ultimate test in all situations that are brought before us is to first sift that circumstance, need, trial, or hurt before the Lord prior to taking action.

Action Steps
1. For each difficulty that arises in your daily situation, practice entering into your "throne room" and committing to see God's point of view before carrying through on any decisions.
2. Pray without ceasing—using a dialogue with God in moment-by-moment decisions and needs.

KNOWING GOD'S WILL

In codependence we were fundamentally unable to make choices that aligned with the legitimate needs in our lives. In fact, we were often consumed with so many external events and relational needs outside of ourselves, that we lost any sense of personal direction based on our choices—or the needs and wants of others.

Through recovery, God wishes to remove the unhealthy activity of our outer courts and replace it with the wisdom and resources to fulfill His plan for us. In discerning the will of God, we can easily feel confused and unsure of what to do or where to go. To help us better understand God's will, we looked at some key points. In assessing our decisions, we can learn to run everything through this filter. While initially this may seem overwhelming, over time, understanding the freedom of being in God's will gives us confidence in our decision-making.

Can you identify where decision-making is the most difficult for you? Why do you think that is?

_____

_____

_____

What is God equipping you with to change this area of your life?

_____

_____

_____

Action Steps

Pray for God's will in all issues and decisions, believing that in trusting Him, He will guide and direct you into healthy choices.

CHAPTER 19
DRESSING FOR SUCCESS

Based on Chapter 19 of *A House that Grace Built*

Ongoing recovery does not happen simply by changing our external behaviors. It involves a far deeper process of developing character. Through God's Word we are introduced to the theme of "putting off the old" and "putting on the new." We "die" to our lifestyle of self-sufficiency so we can rise and live in the lifestyle of God dependence. This is actually how we experience "success" in the Christian life—by "wearing" the very heart and character of God.

How this exactly will appear in our lives may vary. We each bring with us our unique areas of weaknesses and vulnerabilities. Therefore, we must not compare our own character development with those around us. In assessing where and how we need to grow in character and in God's love, we can live with a continual sense of needing God's resources; thus, we are being dependent on Him!

Above all other attributes, love will be the outworking of everything that God does. This love will appear in a form altogether different from our codependence. It will be a love that aligns with God, and is bringing life-giving resources to those around us.

❧ Chapter Highlights
- Assessing character
- Assessing love

❧ Homework Purpose

By assessing our character weaknesses and committing to openly allow God to reveal the areas of our character that need work, we have the opportunity to continue to change and grow. God never expected us to have it together overnight. His expectation is that we constantly give it to Him so that He can do the transformation.

In this chapter we took a biblical look at love to see how it operates and works. This challenges us to be alert and aware at all times of an important question: am I trying to *do* love, or is God *making* me love.

DRESSED IN CHARACTER

Describe any specific areas where your character needs to be developed.

_____

_____

_____

_____

_____

_____

_____

_____

_____

_____

_____

_____

Are there areas of your character that you recognize needs changing that were not discussed in this chapter? Explain.

_____

_____

_____

_____

_____

_____

_____

_____

_____

_____

_____

ASSESSING LOVE

Love is produced by the Holy Spirit, not our human effort. We cannot mimic the fruit of genuine love. It will have certain ingredients in it that will demonstrate its authenticity, as well as contain absences of dysfunctional relationship skills. Our ability to perceive and identify with real love will assist us in revealing when codependence is used in its place.

We looked at the biblical definition of love, and thus can begin to sift and sort through its characteristics to understand what is happening in our own hearts. As we do this, we must remember that the fundamental truth of love is that we can't "do" it, we must "become" it. And it isn't by striving that this will occur, but only by being engaged and intimate with Jesus on a daily basis.

What aspects of love do you struggle with the most?

_____

_____

_____

_____

_____

_____

Can you see any characteristics of love operating in you now that weren't operating in you before your recovery? How do you think that occurred?

_____

_____

_____

_____

_____

_____

Write down where you need to learn to walk out love in your own life.

_____

_____

_____

_____

_____

_____

_____

Action Steps

1. Pray and ask God to continue showing you where love is working or absent in your life.
2. Commit that area over to God's character, realizing that apart from Him, you are unable to love.

CHAPTER 20
BUILT FOR ETERNITY

Based on Chapter 20 of *A House that Grace Built*

As children of God, we are not bound to things of this world, or limited by the time span God has given us here on earth. Our souls and spirits will last forever, and eventually we'll be given new bodies that will also be eternal. We learned in Chapter 20 that our lives on earth are but a drop in the water. They are a tiny fraction compared to what lies ahead. And like a seed which will be planted in the ground, our lives on earth will directly be harvested in our eternal destiny.

In this lifetime, we are bound with the reality of the physical realm that surrounds us, and the challenges that are imposed upon in many ways. But as we learn to live by the principles in God's Kingdom, we will find that His purposes far extend beyond what we can see with our eyes. God's purposes have eternal value. He isn't consumed by the "here and now," but views everything through an eternal canvas.

God also calls us to be fruitful, and to utilize the gifts and blessings He gave us to plant into the Kingdom of Heaven. This doesn't need to make us fearful or cause us shame, but should encourage us to live spiritually alert.

Chapter Highlights

- Gaining eternal perspective
- Separation from the world
- Working out ministry
- Meeting Jesus

Homework Purpose

As we conclude this workbook, more than anything we want to be secure and kept by the One who created us, and the One we will be returning to once our earthly mission is complete. Chapter 20 asked us to assess our own eternal perspective, and challenged us to live a lifestyle of being prepared. Someday soon we will meet Jesus face to face. Are you ready?

GAINING AN ETERNAL PERSPECTIVE

How have you viewed eternity up until this point in your own recovery? Does it seem detached, or a confident destination point?

_____

_____

_____

How does seeing your life with an eternal canvas affect how you see your circumstances right now?

_____

_____

_____

SEPARATION FROM THE WORLD

In understanding the dramatic difference between the two kingdoms at work in this world, we need to assess how we live and represent God's kingdom in the here and now. Living in the kingdom of God and being separated from the world is hardly about living by rules and regulations. It is clearly an entire mentality and belief system that we must embrace. It furthermore is about the authority system by which we choose to live under. Being under God's authority gives us all the tools and resources necessary to live this life and gain the rewards that God's kingdom offers. But if we are not mindful, we can easily slip into patterns, choices, and overall belief systems that contradict our rightful standing as joint heirs of Christ.

Do you see where you are distinctly separated from the world system? What makes you different from someone who isn't walking with the Lord?

_____

_____

_____

Do you see where you have patterned your life around the culture around us, and have thus succumbed to Satan's kingdom principles unknowingly? Explain.

_____

_____

_____

Walking Out Our Ministry

Since God created us for purpose and equipped us to fulfill His plan, we not only have our tangible needs met, but we also have all the resources required to fulfill God's spiritual calling in our lives. Learning to embrace the ministry and spiritual gifts we have been granted is not just an emotional appeal the Lord makes to us, but it is a command and expectation He has placed in our relationship with Him. He fully expects that we will utilize and multiply what He has entrusted to us!

Learning our own callings, gifts, and placements in the body of Christ doesn't have to come in a dramatic role. But we can be assured that God will provide opportunities to make those gifts known and circumstances where we use them. He will also hold us accountable to how we used what He gave us.

Have you embraced your spiritual gifts and calling? Describe.

_____

_____

_____

Does fear or shame ever stifle your ability to align with God's purpose?

_____

_____

_____

Action Steps
1. Pray and ask God to show you in practical ways how to serve, knowing that right now He wants to devote a season of healing in you so that you will ultimately be far more effective in ministry.
2. Daily ask God for opportunities to serve Him—through your role in your family, your community, and the church.

Meeting Jesus

Close your eyes and imagine meeting Jesus right now. If you were to stand before Him, how do you think He would reward you? Would you know Him intimately? Would your works be accepted? Would anything be burned? Is there anything that makes you feel afraid to meet with Jesus? What is it?

_____

_____

_____

What can you do in your life right now to better plan for Jesus's return?

_____

_____

_____

Is there something you want to do or should do, but have been afraid of "investing the seed"; thus, you have protected it? What is it, and what is stopping you?

_____

_____

_____

If you look at every single relationship in your life, is there one that is unsettled? If that person were to die tomorrow, would you have regrets? If so, is there anything you can do right now to make it right? Do you simply need to pray and trust God to make your own heart right with that person, leaving the results to Him?

_____

_____

_____

Action Step

If you are afraid that you are unprepared to meet Jesus, it's never too late to make a commitment to spend the rest of your life living in Him and for Him. Jesus doesn't want our effort, He just wants us. Pray something like this:

Lord God,

I want to be prepared to meet You in eternity. I have been so consumed with the challenges of my earthly life, that I have failed to understand that my purpose began through You and will come back to You. My entire life is to be given to You. I know You will accept me, but I want to be fully prepared for You. Clean my heart and purify my soul. Teach me how to know You and love You right now. Become a true friend, brother, spouse, and teacher to me so that when we meet face to face, I will be reunited with You in true celebration.

In Jesus's name. Amen.

JOURNAL

WEEK 1

Date: _____

Suggested Bible reading:

Galatians 1-2

Psalm 1

A key truth I learned from Your Word

_____

_____

_____

_____

_____

_____

_____

_____

_____

_____

_____

_____

_____

_____

_____

Show me the right path, Lord; point out the road for me to follow.
- Psalm 25:4

THRONE-ROOM JOURNAL
What I Receive from You

_____

_____

_____

_____

_____

_____

_____

_____

_____

_____

_____

_____

_____

_____

_____

_____

_____

_____

_____

_____

_____

_____

_____

_____

_____

_____

_____

_____

_____

_____

_____

_____

_____

_____

THRONE-ROOM JOURNAL
What I Give to You

_____
_____
_____
_____
_____
_____
_____
_____
_____
_____
_____
_____
_____
_____
_____
_____
_____
_____
_____
_____
_____
_____
_____
_____
_____
_____
_____
_____

WEEK 1

My praise

_____
_____
_____
_____
_____

My thanks

_____
_____
_____
_____
_____

My affection

_____
_____
_____
_____
_____

My obedience

_____
_____
_____
_____
_____

WEEK 2

Date: _____

Suggested Bible reading:

Galatians 3-4

Psalm 3-4

A key truth I learned from Your Word

_____

_____

_____

_____

_____

_____

_____

_____

_____

_____

_____

_____

_____

_____

Point out anything in me that offends you, and lead me along the path of everlasting life - Psalm 139:24

THRONE-ROOM JOURNAL
What I Receive from You

THRONE-ROOM JOURNAL
What I Give to You

_____

_____

_____

_____

_____

_____

_____

_____

_____

_____

_____

_____

_____

_____

_____

_____

_____

_____

_____

_____

_____

_____

_____

_____

_____

_____

_____

_____

WEEK 2

My praise

_____

_____

_____

_____

_____

My thanks

_____

_____

_____

_____

_____

My affection

_____

_____

_____

_____

_____

My obedience

_____

_____

_____

_____

_____

_____

_____

WEEK 3

Date:

_____

Suggested Bible reading:

Galatians 4-6

Psalm 5-6

A key truth I learned from Your Word

_____

_____

_____

_____

_____

_____

_____

_____

_____

_____

_____

_____

_____

You will show me the way of life, granting me the joy of your presence and the pleasures of living with you forever.- Psalm 16:11

THRONE-ROOM JOURNAL
What I Receive from You

Throne-Room Journal
What I Give to You

_____
_____
_____
_____
_____
_____
_____
_____
_____
_____
_____
_____
_____
_____
_____
_____
_____
_____
_____
_____
_____
_____
_____
_____
_____
_____
_____
_____

Week 3

My praise
_____
_____
_____
_____
_____

My thanks
_____
_____
_____
_____

My affection
_____
_____
_____
_____

My obedience
_____
_____
_____
_____
_____
_____
_____

WEEK 4

Date:

_____

Bible reading:

Ephesians 1-2

Psalm 7-8

A key truth I learned from Your Word

_____

_____

_____

_____

_____

_____

_____

_____

_____

_____

_____

But as for me, God will redeem my life.
- Psalm 49:15

THRONE-ROOM JOURNAL
What I Receive from You

THRONE-ROOM JOURNAL
What I Give to You

_____
_____
_____
_____
_____
_____
_____
_____
_____
_____
_____
_____
_____
_____
_____
_____
_____
_____
_____
_____
_____
_____
_____
_____
_____
_____
_____
_____
_____

WEEK 4

My praise

_____
_____
_____
_____
_____

My thanks

_____
_____
_____
_____
_____

My affection

_____
_____
_____
_____

My obedience

_____
_____
_____
_____
_____
_____
_____
_____

WEEK 5

Date:

_____

Bible reading:

Ephesians 3-4

Psalm 9-10

A key truth I learned from Your Word

_____

_____

_____

_____

_____

_____

_____

_____

_____

_____

_____

_____

_____

I will study your commandments and reflect on your ways. - Psalm 119:15

THRONE-ROOM JOURNAL
What I Receive from You

THRONE-ROOM JOURNAL
What I Give to You

My praise

_____

_____

_____

_____

_____

My thanks

_____

_____

_____

_____

My affection

_____

_____

_____

_____

My obedience

_____

_____

_____

_____

_____

_____

WEEK 6

Date:

_____

Bible reading:

Ephesians 5-6

Psalm 11-12

A key truth I learned from Your Word

_____

_____

_____

_____

_____

_____

_____

_____

_____

_____

_____

_____

The Lord is my rock, my fortress, and my savior; my God is my rock, in whom I find protection.
- Psalm 18:2

THRONE-ROOM JOURNAL
What I Receive from You

THRONE-ROOM JOURNAL
What I Give to You

My praise

My thanks

My affection

My obedience

WEEK 7

Date:

_____

Bible reading:

Philippians 1-2

Psalm 13-14

A key truth I learned from Your Word

_____

_____

_____

_____

_____

_____

_____

_____

_____

_____

_____

_____

_____

_____

_____

I have swept away your sins like a cloud. I have scattered your offenses like the morning mist. Oh, return to me, for I have paid the price to set you free."

- Isaiah 44:22

THRONE-ROOM JOURNAL
What I Receive from You

THRONE-ROOM JOURNAL
What I Give to You

My praise

_____

_____

_____

_____

_____

My thanks

_____

_____

_____

_____

My affection

_____

_____

_____

_____

My obedience

_____

_____

_____

_____

_____

_____

WEEK 8

Date:

_____

Bible reading:

Philippians 3-4

Psalm 15-16

A key truth I learned from Your Word

_____

_____

_____

_____

_____

_____

_____

_____

_____

_____

_____

For every child of God defeats this evil world, and we achieve this victory through our faith.
- 1 John 5:4

THRONE-ROOM JOURNAL
What I Receive from You

THRONE-ROOM JOURNAL
What I Give to You

_____
_____
_____
_____
_____
_____
_____
_____
_____
_____
_____
_____
_____
_____
_____
_____
_____
_____
_____
_____
_____
_____
_____
_____
_____
_____
_____
_____
_____
_____
_____

WEEK 8

My praise
_____
_____
_____
_____
_____

My thanks
_____
_____
_____
_____

My affection
_____
_____
_____
_____

My obedience
_____
_____
_____
_____
_____
_____
_____

WEEK 9

Date:

_____

Bible reading:

Colossians 1-2

Psalm 17-18

A key truth I learned from Your Word

_____

_____

_____

_____

_____

_____

_____

_____

_____

_____

I will instruct you and teach you in the way you should go; I will counsel you and watch over you. - Psalm 32:8

THRONE-ROOM JOURNAL
What I Receive from You

THRONE-ROOM JOURNAL
What I Give to You

WEEK 9

My praise

My thanks

My affection

My obedience

WEEK 10

Date:

_____

Bible reading:

Colossians 3-4

Psalm 19-20

A key truth I learned from Your Word

_____

_____

_____

_____

_____

_____

_____

_____

_____

_____

_____

_____

But the eyes of the LORD are on those who fear him, on those whose hope is in his unfailing love.
- Psalm 33:18

THRONE-ROOM JOURNAL
What I Receive from You

THRONE-ROOM JOURNAL
What I Give to You

My praise

_____

_____

_____

_____

_____

My thanks

_____

_____

_____

_____

My affection

_____

_____

_____

_____

My obedience

_____

_____

_____

_____

_____

_____

WEEK 11

Date:

_____

Bible reading:

John 1-2

Psalm 21-22

A key truth I learned from Your Word

_____

_____

_____

_____

_____

_____

_____

_____

_____

_____

_____

Come, my children, and listen to me, and I will teach you to fear the Lord. - Psalm 34:11

THRONE-ROOM JOURNAL
What I Receive from You

_____

_____

_____

_____

_____

_____

_____

_____

_____

_____

_____

_____

_____

_____

_____

_____

_____

_____

_____

_____

_____

_____

_____

_____

_____

_____

_____

_____

_____

_____

_____

_____

THRONE-ROOM JOURNAL
What I Give to You

My praise

_____
_____
_____
_____
_____

My thanks

_____
_____
_____
_____

My affection

_____
_____
_____
_____

My obedience

_____
_____
_____
_____
_____
_____

WEEK 12

Date:

_____

Bible reading:

John 3-4

Psalm 23-24

A key truth I learned from Your Word

_____

_____

_____

_____

_____

_____

_____

_____

_____

_____

_____

_____

_____

Fear of the Lord is the foundation of true wisdom. All who obey his commandments will grow in wisdom. Praise him forever! - Psalm 11:12

THRONE-ROOM JOURNAL
What I Receive from You

THRONE-ROOM JOURNAL
What I Give to You

My praise

_____

_____

_____

_____

_____

My thanks

_____

_____

_____

_____

_____

My affection

_____

_____

_____

_____

_____

My obedience

_____

_____

_____

_____

_____

_____

WEEK 13

Date:

_____

Bible reading:

John 5-6

Psalm 25-26

A key truth I learned from Your Word

_____

_____

_____

_____

_____

_____

_____

_____

_____

_____

_____

_____

_____

Lord, don't hold back your tender mercies from me. Let your unfailing love and faithfulness always protect me.

- Psalm 40:11

THRONE-ROOM JOURNAL
What I Receive from You

THRONE-ROOM JOURNAL
What I Give to You

My praise

_____

_____

_____

_____

_____

My thanks

_____

_____

_____

_____

_____

My affection

_____

_____

_____

_____

_____

My obedience

_____

_____

_____

_____

_____

_____

_____

WEEK 14

Date:

_____

Bible reading:

John 7-8

Psalm 27-28

A key truth I learned from Your Word

_____

_____

_____

_____

_____

_____

_____

_____

_____

_____

_____

_____

_____

How precious is your unfailing love, O God! All humanity finds shelter in the shadow of your wings. - Psalm 36:7

THRONE-ROOM JOURNAL
What I Receive from You

THRONE-ROOM JOURNAL
What I Give to You

_____
_____
_____
_____
_____
_____
_____
_____
_____
_____
_____
_____
_____
_____
_____
_____
_____
_____
_____
_____
_____
_____
_____
_____
_____
_____
_____
_____
_____

WEEK 14

My praise

_____
_____
_____
_____

My thanks

_____
_____
_____
_____

My affection

_____
_____
_____
_____

My obedience

_____
_____
_____
_____
_____
_____
_____

WEEK 15

Date:

_____

Bible reading:

John 9-10

Psalm 29-30

A key truth I learned from Your Word

_____

_____

_____

_____

_____

_____

_____

_____

_____

_____

_____

_____

_____

Let anyone who is thirsty come. Let anyone who desires drink freely from the water of life.
- Revelations 22:17

THRONE-ROOM JOURNAL
What I Receive from You

THRONE-ROOM JOURNAL
What I Give to You

My praise

My thanks

My affection

My obedience

WEEK 16

Date:

_____

Bible reading:

John 11-12

Psalm 31-32

A key truth I learned from Your Word

_____

_____

_____

_____

_____

_____

_____

_____

_____

_____

_____

_____

_____

Be on guard. Stand firm in the faith. Be courageous. Be strong.
- 1 Corinthians 16:13

THRONE-ROOM JOURNAL
What I Receive from You

THRONE-ROOM JOURNAL
What I Give to You

My praise

_____

_____

_____

_____

_____

My thanks

_____

_____

_____

_____

_____

My affection

_____

_____

_____

_____

My obedience

_____

_____

_____

_____

_____

_____

WEEK 17

Date:

_____

Bible reading:

John 13-14

Psalm 33-34

A key truth I learned from Your Word

_____

_____

_____

_____

_____

_____

_____

_____

_____

_____

_____

_____

Fearing people is a dangerous trap, but trusting the Lord means safety.
- Proverbs 29:25

THRONE-ROOM JOURNAL
What I Receive from You

THRONE-ROOM JOURNAL
What I Give to You

My praise

_____

_____

_____

_____

_____

My thanks

_____

_____

_____

_____

_____

My affection

_____

_____

_____

_____

_____

My obedience

_____

_____

_____

_____

_____

_____

_____

WEEK 18

Date:

_____

Bible reading:

John 15-16

Psalm 35-36

A key truth I learned from Your Word

_____

_____

_____

_____

_____

_____

_____

_____

_____

_____

_____

_____

_____

Those who live in the shelter of the Most High will find rest in the shadow of the Almighty. - Psalm 91:1

THRONE-ROOM JOURNAL
What I Receive from You

THRONE-ROOM JOURNAL
What I Give to You

My praise

_____

_____

_____

_____

_____

My thanks

_____

_____

_____

_____

_____

My affection

_____

_____

_____

_____

_____

My obedience

_____

_____

_____

_____

_____

_____

_____

_____

WEEK 19

Date:

_____

Bible reading:

John 17-18

Psalm 37-38

A key truth I learned from Your Word

_____

_____

_____

_____

_____

_____

_____

_____

_____

_____

_____

_____

_____

_____

Such love has no fear, because perfect love expels all fear.
- 1 John 4:18

THRONE-ROOM JOURNAL
What I Receive from You

THRONE-ROOM JOURNAL
What I Give to You

My praise

_____

_____

_____

_____

_____

My thanks

_____

_____

_____

_____

_____

My affection

_____

_____

_____

_____

My obedience

_____

_____

_____

_____

_____

_____

_____

WEEK 20

Date:

_____

Bible reading:

John 19-20

Psalm 39-40

A key truth I learned from Your Word

_____

_____

_____

_____

_____

_____

_____

_____

_____

_____

_____

_____

_____

Some of you will rebuild the deserted ruins of your cities. Then you will be known as a rebuilder of walls and a restorer of homes. - Isaiah 58:12

THRONE-ROOM JOURNAL
What I Give to You

My praise

_____

_____

_____

_____

_____

_____

My thanks

_____

_____

_____

_____

_____

My affection

_____

_____

_____

_____

_____

My obedience

_____

_____

_____

_____

_____

_____

WEEK 21

Date:

_____

Bible reading:

John 21

Psalm 41-42

A key truth I learned from Your Word

_____

_____

_____

_____

_____

_____

_____

_____

_____

_____

_____

_____

And let the peace that comes from Christ rule in your hearts.
- Colossians 3:15

THRONE-ROOM JOURNAL
What I Receive from You

THRONE-ROOM JOURNAL
What I Give to You

WEEK 21

My praise

My thanks

My affection

My obedience

WEEK 22

Date:

_____

Bible reading:

Romans 1-2

Psalm 43-44

A key truth I learned from Your Word

_____

_____

_____

_____

_____

_____

_____

_____

_____

_____

_____

For your Creator will be your husband; the Lord of Heaven's Armies is his name!
- Isaiah 54:5

THRONE-ROOM JOURNAL
What I Receive from You

THRONE-ROOM JOURNAL
What I Give to You

My praise

My thanks

My affection

My obedience

WEEK 23

Date:

_____

Bible reading:

Romans 3-4

Psalm 45-46

A key truth I learned from Your Word

_____

_____

_____

_____

_____

_____

_____

_____

_____

_____

_____

For all who are led by the Spirit of God are children of God. - Romans 8:14

THRONE-ROOM JOURNAL
What I Receive from You

THRONE-ROOM JOURNAL
What I Give to You

_____

_____

_____

_____

_____

_____

_____

_____

_____

_____

_____

_____

_____

_____

_____

_____

_____

_____

_____

_____

_____

_____

_____

_____

_____

_____

_____

WEEK 23

My praise

_____

_____

_____

_____

_____

My thanks

_____

_____

_____

_____

_____

My affection

_____

_____

_____

_____

_____

My obedience

_____

_____

_____

_____

_____

_____

_____

WEEK 24

Date:

_____

Bible reading:

Romans 5-6

Psalm 47-48

A key truth I learned from Your Word

_____

_____

_____

_____

_____

_____

_____

_____

_____

_____

_____

_____

"But to you who are willing to listen, I say, love your enemies! Do good to those who hate you. - Luke 6:27

THRONE-ROOM JOURNAL
What I Give to You

My praise

My thanks

My affection

My obedience

WEEK 25

Date:

_____

Bible reading:

Romans 7-8

Psalm 49-50

A key truth I learned from Your Word

_____

_____

_____

_____

_____

_____

_____

_____

_____

_____

_____

_____

_____

_____

"I am leaving you with a gift--peace of mind and heart. And the peace I give is a gift the world cannot give. So don't be troubled or afraid. - John 14:27

THRONE-ROOM JOURNAL
What I Receive from You

THRONE-ROOM JOURNAL
What I Give to You

_____
_____
_____
_____
_____
_____
_____
_____
_____
_____
_____
_____
_____
_____
_____
_____
_____
_____
_____
_____
_____
_____
_____
_____
_____
_____
_____

WEEK 25

My praise

_____
_____
_____
_____
_____

My thanks

_____
_____
_____
_____

My affection

_____
_____
_____
_____

My obedience

_____
_____
_____
_____
_____
_____

WEEK 26

Date:

_____

Bible reading:

Romans 9

Psalm 51-52

A key truth I learned from Your Word

_____

_____

_____

_____

_____

_____

_____

_____

_____

_____

_____

For that is what God is like. He is our God forever and ever, and he will guide us until we die. - Psalm 48:14

THRONE-ROOM JOURNAL
What I Receive from You

THRONE-ROOM JOURNAL
What I Give to You

WEEK 26

My praise

_____

_____

_____

_____

_____

My thanks

_____

_____

_____

_____

My affection

_____

_____

_____

_____

My obedience

_____

_____

_____

_____

_____

_____

WEEK 27

Date:

_____

Bible reading:

Romans 10-11

Psalm 53-54

A key truth I learned from Your Word

_____

_____

_____

_____

_____

_____

_____

_____

_____

_____

_____

_____

Exalt the Lord our God! Bow low before his feet, for he is holy! - Psalm 99:5

THRONE-ROOM JOURNAL
What I Receive from You

THRONE-ROOM JOURNAL
What I Give to You

_____
_____
_____
_____
_____
_____
_____
_____
_____
_____
_____
_____
_____
_____
_____
_____
_____
_____
_____
_____
_____
_____
_____
_____
_____
_____
_____

WEEK 27

My praise

_____
_____
_____
_____
_____

My thanks

_____
_____
_____
_____
_____

My affection

_____
_____
_____
_____
_____

My obedience

_____
_____
_____
_____
_____
_____
_____

Date:

_____

Bible reading:

Romans 12-13

Psalm 55-56

A key truth I learned from Your Word

_____

_____

_____

_____

_____

_____

_____

_____

_____

_____

_____

_____

_____

_____

_____

_____

Create in me a clean heart, O God. Renew a loyal spirit within me.
- Psalm 51:19

THRONE-ROOM JOURNAL
What I Receive from You

THRONE-ROOM JOURNAL
What I Give to You

WEEK 28

My praise

My thanks

My affection

My obedience

WEEK 29

Date:

_____

Bible reading:

Romans 14-15

Psalm 57-58

A key truth I learned from Your Word

_____

_____

_____

_____

_____

_____

_____

_____

_____

_____

_____

_____

_____

_____

God blesses those whose hearts are pure, for they will see God. - Matthew 5:8

THRONE-ROOM JOURNAL
What I Receive from You

THRONE-ROOM JOURNAL
What I Give to You

_____
_____
_____
_____
_____
_____
_____
_____
_____
_____
_____
_____
_____
_____
_____
_____
_____
_____
_____
_____
_____
_____
_____
_____
_____

My praise

_____
_____
_____
_____

My thanks

_____
_____
_____
_____

My affection

_____
_____
_____
_____

My obedience

_____
_____
_____
_____
_____

WEEK 30

Date:

_____

Bible reading:

Romans 16

Psalm 59-60

A key truth I learned from Your Word

_____

_____

_____

_____

_____

_____

_____

_____

_____

_____

_____

_____

_____

He will wipe every tear from their eyes, and there will be no more death or sorrow or crying or pain.
- Revelation 21:4

THRONE-ROOM JOURNAL
What I Receive from You

THRONE-ROOM JOURNAL
What I Give to You

My praise

My thanks

My affection

My obedience

27387668R00113

Made in the USA
San Bernardino, CA
13 December 2015